*Polished Spiral* Karin Kuhlmann

"Although the creation of fractals is bounded to strict mathematical rules, the results
are always very inspiring."– **Karin Kuhlmann**

GRADE

**4**

# Describing the Shape of the Data

Data Analysis and Probability

UNIT **2**

# Investigations

### IN NUMBER, DATA, AND SPACE®

**Editorial offices:** Glenview, Illinois • Parsippany, New Jersey • New York, New York
**Sales offices:** Boston, Massachusetts • Duluth, Georgia
Glenview, Illinois • Coppell, Texas • Sacramento, California • Mesa, Arizona

scottforesman.com

The Investigations curriculum was developed by TERC, Cambridge, MA.

T E R C

This material is based on work supported by the National Science Foundation ("NSF") under Grant No. ESI-0095450. Any opinions, findings, and conclusions or recommendations expressed in this material are those of the author(s) and do not necessarily reflect the views of the National Science Foundation.

ISBN: 0-328-23754-X

ISBN: 978-0-328-23754-8

**Second Edition Copyright © 2008 Pearson Education, Inc.**
All Rights Reserved. Printed in the United States of America. This publication is protected by Copyright, and permission should be obtained from the publisher prior to any prohibited reproduction, storage in a retrieval system, or transmission in any form by any means, electronic, mechanical, photocopying, recording, or otherwise. For information regarding permission(s), write to: Permissions Department, Scott Foresman, 1900 East Lake Avenue, Glenview, Illinois 60025.

7 8 9 10-V003-15 14 13 12 11 10 09 08
CC:N2

**TERC**

## Co-Principal Investigators
Susan Jo Russell

Karen Economopoulos

## Authors
Lucy Wittenberg
Director Grades 3–5

Karen Economopoulos
Director Grades K–2

Virginia Bastable
(SummerMath for Teachers,
Mt. Holyoke College)

Katie Hickey Bloomfield

Keith Cochran

Darrell Earnest

Arusha Hollister

Nancy Horowitz

Erin Leidl

Megan Murray

Young Oh

Beth W. Perry

Susan Jo Russell

Deborah Schifter
(Education
Development Center)

Kathy Sillman

## Administrative Staff
Amy Taber
Project Manager

Beth Bergeron

Lorraine Brooks

Emi Fujiwara

## Contributing Authors
Denise Baumann

Jennifer DiBrienza

Hollee Freeman

Paula Hooper

Jan Mokros

Stephen Monk
(University of Washington)

Mary Beth O'Connor

Judy Storeygard

Cornelia Tierney

Elizabeth Van Cleef

Carol Wright

## Technology
Jim Hammerman

## Classroom Field Work
Amy Appell

Rachel E. Davis

Traci Higgins

Julia Thompson

## Collaborating Teachers
This group of dedicated teachers carried out extensive field testing in their classrooms, met regularly to discuss issues of teaching and learning mathematics, provided feedback to staff, welcomed staff into their classrooms to document students' work, and contributed both suggestions and written material that has been incorporated into the curriculum.

| | |
|---|---|
| Bethany Altchek | Maura McGrail |
| Linda Amaral | Kathe Millett |
| Kimberly Beauregard | Florence Molyneaux |
| Barbara Bernard | Amy Monkiewicz |
| Nancy Buell | Elizabeth Monopoli |
| Rose Christiansen | Carol Murray |
| Chris Colbath-Hess | Robyn Musser |
| Lisette Colon | Christine Norrman |
| Kim Cook | Deborah O'Brien |
| Frances Cooper | Timothy O'Connor |
| Kathleen Drew | Anne Marie O'Reilly |
| Rebeka Eston Salemi | Mark Paige |
| Thomas Fisher | Margaret Riddle |
| Michael Flynn | Karen Schweitzer |
| Holly Ghazey | Elisabeth Seyferth |
| Susan Gillis | Susan Smith |
| Danielle Harrington | Debra Sorvillo |
| Elaine Herzog | Shoshanah Starr |
| Francine Hiller | Janice Szymaszek |
| Kirsten Lee Howard | Karen Tobin |
| Liliana Klass | JoAnn Trauschke |
| Leslie Kramer | Ana Vaisenstein |
| Melissa Lee Andrichak | Yvonne Watson |
| Kelley Lee Sadowski | Michelle Woods |
| Jennifer Levitan | Mary Wright |
| Mary Lou LoVecchio | |
| Kristen McEnaney | |

Note: Unless otherwise noted, all contributors listed above were staff of the Education Research Collaborative at TERC during their work on the curriculum. Other affiliations during the time of development are listed.

## Advisors

Deborah Lowenberg Ball,
University of Michigan

Hyman Bass, Professor of Mathematics and Mathematics Education
University of Michigan

Mary Canner, Principal, Natick Public Schools

Thomas Carpenter, Professor of Curriculum and Instruction,
University of Wisconsin-Madison

Janis Freckmann, Elementary Mathematics Coordinator,
Milwaukee Public Schools

Lynne Godfrey, Mathematics Coach,
Cambridge Public Schools

Ginger Hanlon, Instructional Specialist in Mathematics,
New York City Public Schools

DeAnn Huinker, Director, Center for Mathematics and
Science Education Research, University of Wisconsin-Milwaukee

James Kaput, Professor of Mathematics, University of
Massachusetts-Dartmouth

Kate Kline, Associate Professor, Department of Mathematics
and Statistics, Western Michigan University

Jim Lewis, Professor of Mathematics,
University of Nebraska-Lincoln

William McCallum, Professor of Mathematics,
University of Arizona

Harriet Pollatsek, Professor of Mathematics,
Mount Holyoke College

Debra Shein-Gerson, Elementary Mathematics Specialist,
Weston Public Schools

Gary Shevell, Assistant Principal,
New York City Public Schools

Liz Sweeney, Elementary Math Department,
Boston Public Schools

Lucy West, Consultant, Metamorphosis:
Teaching Learning Communities, Inc.

This revision of the curriculum was built on the work of the many authors who contributed to the first edition (published between 1994 and 1998). We acknowledge the critical contributions of these authors in developing the content and pedagogy of *Investigations*:

## Authors

Joan Akers

Michael T. Battista

Douglas H. Clements

Karen Economopoulos

Marlene Kliman

Jan Mokros

Megan Murray

Ricardo Nemirovsky

Andee Rubin

Susan Jo Russell

Cornelia Tierney

## Contributing Authors

Mary Berle-Carman

Rebecca B. Corwin

Rebeka Eston

Claryce Evans

Anne Goodrow

Cliff Konold

Chris Mainhart

Sue McMillen

Jerrie Moffet

Tracy Noble

Kim O'Neil

Mark Ogonowski

Julie Sarama

Amy Shulman Weinberg

Margie Singer

Virginia Woolley

Tracey Wright

# Contents

## UNIT 2

# Describing the Shape of the Data

### INTRODUCTION AND OVERVIEW

| | |
|---|---|
| Investigations Curriculum | 6 |
| Overview of This Unit | 8 |
| Mathematics in This Unit | 10 |
| Assessment in This Unit | 14 |
| Ten-Minute Math in This Unit | 16 |
| Practice and Review in This Unit | 17 |
| Differentiation in This Unit | 18 |

### INVESTIGATION 1

## Landmarks in the Data

| | |
|---|---|
| INVESTIGATION 1 PLANNER | 20 |
| SESSION 1.1 How Many Raisins in a Box? | 22 |
| SESSION 1.2 How Tall Are Fourth Graders? | 30 |
| SESSION 1.3 How Tall Are First Graders? | 36 |
| SESSION 1.4 Comparing the Heights of Fourth and First Graders | 41 |
| SESSION 1.5 Assessment: Comparing Numbers of Cavities | 46 |

### INVESTIGATION 2

## Using Data to Compare

| | |
|---|---|
| INVESTIGATION 2 PLANNER | 52 |
| SESSION 2.1 What Do We Want to Find Out? | 56 |
| SESSION 2.2 Assessment: Collecting and Comparing Data | 62 |
| SESSION 2.3 Representing Survey Data | 67 |
| SESSION 2.4 What Did You Learn from Your Survey? | 71 |
| SESSION 2.5 Mystery Data | 75 |
| SESSION 2.6 Comparing WNBA Players' Points Per Game | 81 |
| SESSION 2.7 Is This a Good Game? | 87 |

### INVESTIGATION 3

## Finding and Comparing Probabilities

| | |
|---|---|
| INVESTIGATION 3 PLANNER | 92 |
| SESSION 3.1 Creating a Likelihood Line | 94 |
| SESSION 3.2 Numerical Measures of Probability | 101 |
| SESSION 3.3 Probability Experiments | 107 |
| SESSION 3.4 Comparing Probability Experiments | 113 |
| SESSION 3.5 End-of-Unit Assessment | 117 |

| | |
|---|---|
| Teacher Notes | 121 |
| Dialogue Boxes | 144 |
| Student Math Handbook | 154 |
| Index | 158 |

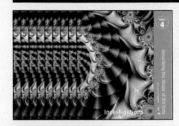

## C U R R I C U L U M

## Overview of Program Components

**FOR TEACHERS**

The **Curriculum Units** are the teaching guides. (See far right.)

**Implementing Investigations in Grade 4** offers suggestions for implementing the curriculum. It also contains a comprehensive index.

The **Resources Binder** contains all the Resource Masters and Transparencies that support instruction. (Also available on CD) The binder also includes a student software CD.

**FOR STUDENTS**

The **Student Activity Book** contains the consumable student pages (Recording Sheets, Homework, Practice, and so on).

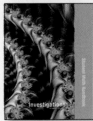

The **Student Math Handbook** contains Math Words and Ideas pages and Games directions.

## The *Investigations* Curriculum

*Investigations in Number, Data, and Space*® is a K–5 mathematics curriculum designed to engage students in making sense of mathematical ideas. Six major goals guided the development of the *Investigations in Number, Data, and Space*® curriculum. The curriculum is designed to:

- Support students to make sense of mathematics and learn that they can be mathematical thinkers

- Focus on computational fluency with whole numbers as a major goal of the elementary grades

- Provide substantive work in important areas of mathematics—rational numbers, geometry, measurement, data, and early algebra—and connections among them

- Emphasize reasoning about mathematical ideas

- Communicate mathematics content and pedagogy to teachers

- Engage the range of learners in understanding mathematics

Underlying these goals are three guiding principles that are touchstones for the *Investigations* team as we approach both students and teachers as agents of their own learning:

1. *Students have mathematical ideas.* Students come to school with ideas about numbers, shapes, measurements, patterns, and data. If given the opportunity to learn in an environment that stresses making sense of mathematics, students build on the ideas they already have and learn about new mathematics they have never encountered. Students learn that they are capable of having mathematical ideas, applying what they know to new situations, and thinking and reasoning about unfamiliar problems.

2. *Teachers are engaged in ongoing learning* about mathematics content, pedagogy, and student learning. The curriculum provides material for professional development, to be used by teachers individually or in groups, that supports teachers' continued learning as they use the curriculum over several years. The *Investigations* curriculum materials are designed as much to be a dialogue with teachers as to be a core of content for students.

3. *Teachers collaborate with the students and curriculum materials* to create the curriculum as enacted in the classroom. The only way for a good curriculum to be used well is for teachers to be active participants in implementing it. Teachers use the curriculum to maintain a clear, focused, and coherent agenda for mathematics teaching. At the same time, they observe and listen carefully to students, try to understand how they are thinking, and make teaching decisions based on these observations.

*Investigations* is based on experience from research and practice, including field testing that involved documentation of thousands of hours in classrooms, observations of students, input from teachers, and analysis of student work. As a result, the curriculum addresses the learning needs of real students in a wide range of classrooms and communities. The investigations are carefully designed to invite all students into mathematics—girls and boys; members of diverse cultural, ethnic, and language groups; and students with a wide variety of strengths, needs, and interests.

Based on this extensive classroom testing, the curriculum takes seriously the time students need to develop a strong conceptual foundation and skills based on that foundation. Each curriculum unit focuses on an area of content in depth, providing time for students to develop and practice ideas across a variety of activities and contexts that build on each other. Daily guidelines for time spent on class sessions, Classroom Routines (K–3), and Ten-Minute Math (3–5) reflect the commitment to devoting adequate time to mathematics in each school day.

## About This Curriculum Unit

This **Curriculum Unit** is one of nine teaching guides in Grade 4. The second unit in Grade 4 is *Describing the Shape of the Data.*

- The **Introduction and Overview** section organizes and presents the instructional materials, provides background information, and highlights important features specific to this unit.

- Each Curriculum Unit contains several **Investigations.** Each Investigation focuses on a set of related mathematical ideas.

- Investigations are divided into one-hour **Sessions,** or lessons.

- Sessions have a combination of these parts: **Activity, Discussion, Math Workshop, Assessment Activity,** and **Session Follow-Up.**

- Each session also has one or more **Ten-Minute Math** activities that are done outside of math time.

- At the back of the book is a collection of **Teacher Notes** and **Dialogue Boxes** that provide professional development related to the unit.

- Also included at the back of the book are the **Student Math Handbook** pages for this unit.

- The **Index** provides a way to look up important words or terms.

# Overview

## OF THIS UNIT

| Investigation | | Session | Day | |
|---|---|---|---|---|
| **INVESTIGATION 1**<br>**Landmarks in the Data**<br>Students record, organize, and represent data, including measuring the heights of first and fourth graders. They learn to use the median as one way to describe and compare data sets. | **1.1** How Many Raisins in a Box? | | 1 | |
| | **1.2** How Tall Are Fourth Graders? | | 2 | |
| | **1.3** How Tall Are First Graders? | | 3 | |
| | **1.4** Comparing the Heights of Fourth and First Graders | | 4 | |
| | **1.5** Assessment: Comparing Numbers of Cavities | | 5 | |
| **INVESTIGATION 2**<br>**Using Data to Compare**<br>Students choose their own survey questions for data collection. They represent and analyze the data. They also draw conclusions based on evidence in different sets of data. | **2.1** What Do We Want to Find Out? | | 6 | |
| | **2.2** Assessment: Collecting and Comparing Data | | 7 | |
| | **2.3** Representing Survey Data | | 8 | |
| | **2.4** What Did You Learn from Your Survey? | | 9 | |
| | **2.5** Mystery Data | | 10 | |
| | **2.6** Comparing WNBA Players' Points Per Game | | 11 | |
| | **2.7** Is This a Good Game? | | 12 | |
| **INVESTIGATION 3**<br>**Finding and Comparing Probabilities**<br>Students learn to describe probability using words such as *impossible* and *certain,* and the numbers 0 to 1. They conduct probability experiments and describe and compare results. | **3.1** Creating a Likelihood Line | | 13 | |
| | **3.2** Numerical Measures of Probability | | 14 | |
| | **3.3** Probability Experiments | | 15 | |
| | **3.4** Comparing Probability Experiments | | 16 | |
| | **3.5** End-of-Unit Assessment | | 17 | |

Each *Investigations* session has some combination of these five parts: **Activity, Discussion, Math Workshop, Assessment Activity,** and **Session Follow-Up.** These session parts are indicated in the chart below. Each session also has one or more **Ten-Minute Math** activities that are done outside of math time.

| Activity | Discussion | Math Workshop | Assessment Activity | Session Follow-Up |
|---|---|---|---|---|
| ● ● | ● | | | ● |
| ● ● | ● | | | ● |
| ● ● | | | | ● |
| ● | ● | | | ● |
| ● | ● | | ● | ● |
| ● ● | ● | | | ● |
| ● ● | | | ● | ● |
| ● | ● | | | ● |
| ● | ● | | | ● |
| ● | ● | | | ● |
| ● | ● | | | ● |
| ● | ● | | | ● |
| ● ● | ● | | | ● |
| ● ● | ● | | | ● |
| ● | ● | | | ● |
| ● | ● | | | ● |
| | | | ● | ● |

### Ten-Minute Math

| Today's Number: Broken Calculator | Quick Survey |
|---|---|
| ● | |
| ● | |
| ● | |
| | ● |
| | ● |
| ● | |
| ● | |
| | ● |
| ● | |
| ● | |
| ● | |
| | ● |
| ● | |
| ● | |
| | ● |
| | ● |
| ● | |

# Mathematics

**Describing the Shape of the Data** is the fourth-grade unit in the Data Analysis and Probability strand of *Investigations*. These units develop ideas about collecting, representing, describing, and interpreting data and about describing and predicting the likelihood of events

**LOOKING BACK** In Grade 3, students worked with both categorical and numerical data. They represented data by using line plots and bar graphs, carried out their own surveys, and worked with measurement data. They focused on how to develop a good survey question that would result in useful data. Students began their work on seeing and describing a data set as a whole and on using that information to compare groups. Their work emphasized describing where the data were concentrated. *Range* and *mode* were also introduced. Students encountered the *median* for the first time as a measure of center in the data, but understanding and using the median was not a benchmark for Grade 3. Students collected data through both counting and measuring and considered how to measure carefully when collecting data. Probability was not introduced in Grade 3.

**This unit focuses on 5 Mathematical Emphases:**

## 1 Data Analysis  Representing data

### Math Focus Points

◆ Organizing ordered numerical data to describe a data set

◆ Using a line plot to represent ordered numerical data

◆ Representing two sets of data in order to compare them

In order to see and describe the shape of numerical data, the data must be represented in a way that shows their distribution—where the data are concentrated and how they are spread across the range. A *line plot* is a tool for showing the distribution of a set of quantitative data. See **Teacher Note:** Data Terms and Representations, page 121.

Students learned to use line plots in Grade 3 and should be proficient in making and interpreting line plots by the end of this unit. In addition, students work on how to represent data about two groups. Some students use two separate line plots or bar graphs. In this case, they need to think about what helps their audience compare the two graphs—for example, lining up the values so that the shapes of the two distributions can be compared easily. Other students find ways to use a single graph to show both groups. In this case, they have to think through how to make clear which data values belong to each group.

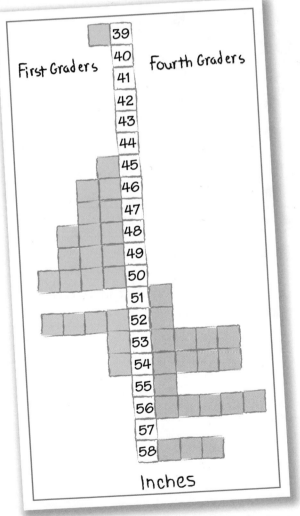

*Sample Student Work*

## 2 Data Analysis  Describing, summarizing, and comparing data

### Math Focus Points

- Describing the shape of a data set: where the data are spread out or concentrated, what the highest and lowest values are, what the range is, and what the outliers are

- Describing what values are typical or atypical in a data set

- Determining the range of a data set

- Describing and interpreting data that compare two groups

- Finding the median of a data set

- Using medians to compare groups

- Considering what information a median does and does not provide

- Comparing two sets of data using the shape and spread of the data

The work in this unit focuses on comparing groups of data. Comparison motivates describing *and* summarizing data. For example, trying to answer the question, "How much taller is a fourth grader than a first grader?" necessitates characterizing each set of data as a whole. In order to describe a group as a whole, it is not satisfactory to simply list all the data values (2 students are 51 inches tall, 6 students are 52 inches tall, 5 students are 56 inches tall, etc.). Students consider how to characterize each group. For example, "First graders are generally between 45 and 52 inches tall, and over $\frac{3}{4}$ of the fourth graders are between 53 and 58 inches, so the fourth graders are about 6 or 7 inches taller overall," or, "The median height of the fourth graders is 54 inches, so half of the fourth graders are 54 inches or taller; only one of the first graders is 54 inches,

and that is the tallest first grader; comparing the medians, I'd say the fourth graders are about 5 inches taller as a group." In this unit, students strengthen their skills in describing the data and move toward summarizing the data—choosing the most important features that characterize a data set. In this context, they use the median as one feature that can help them summarize the data.

## 3 Data Analysis  Analyzing and interpreting data

### Math Focus Points

- Developing arguments based on data

- Drawing conclusions based on data

Data are collected in a context and for a purpose. Data are used to answer a question, to investigate an issue, or to provide information about something in the world that is of interest. But after data have been collected, represented, and summarized, the question remains: What do the data tell us? What do we know, on the basis of the evidence we have collected? Do the data, in fact, provide information about the phenomenon they represent? For example, after students have collected data about the heights of first and fourth graders, what conclusions can they draw? In this unit, students develop conclusions and make arguments based on evidence they have collected. In Investigation 2, they study the points scored by two basketball players in the WNBA during a season. Can these data be used to answer questions such as whether a particular game was a "good game" for one of the players or which player had a better season? Throughout this unit, students learn to support their conclusions and arguments with evidence from the data.

## **4** Data Analysis Designing and carrying out a data investigation

### Math Focus Points

◆ Recording and keeping track of data

◆ Considering how well a data representation communicates to an audience

◆ Developing and revising a survey question

In every grade, students carry out their own data investigations, but in each grade level, what they are asked to do grows in complexity. In this unit, students develop questions of their own that involve collecting numerical data and comparing two groups. They decide on, try out, and refine their questions; decide what group to compare to their own class; keep track of their data for both groups; and figure out how they can represent data for two groups. After their data have been collected, they consider whether their data do, in fact, provide information about their original question. By carrying out a complete data investigation from formulating a question through drawing conclusions from their data, students gain an understanding of data analysis as a tool for learning about the world.

## **5** Probability Describing the probability of an event

### Math Focus Points

◆ Associating the word *probability* with the likelihood of an event

◆ Arranging events along a line representing the range of *certain* to *impossible*

◆ Using numbers from 0 to 1 as measures of probability

◆ Associating verbal descriptions of probability with numeric descriptions

◆ Comparing the expected probability of an event with the actual results of repeated trials of that event

We all deal with uncertainty in our lives every day, so both you and your students have probably developed everyday intuitions about chance events. Research has shown that probability is a notoriously difficult topic well through high school and college, partly because our intuitions are not always in agreement with the mathematics of probability. In the *Investigations* curriculum, we delay working with probability until Grade 4, when students are developing mathematical ideas, such as ideas about fractions, that can help them with this topic. At this grade level, they are also beginning to reason about abstractions such as how the theoretical chance (or *theoretical probability*) of rolling 1 on a number cube is different from what may actually happen when a number cube is rolled repeatedly.

In this unit, students first think about the likelihood of events in their world—what events are impossible, unlikely, likely, or certain. Then they consider situations in which there are a certain number of possible outcomes—such as tossing a coin, rolling a number cube, or pulling a red cube from a bag holding red and blue cubes. The likelihood of each outcome can be expressed as a number from 0 (impossible) to 1 (certain). Students conduct experiments that involve repeating chance events (pulling a colored cube out of a container) many times. Through these probability experiments, students can see that their results are usually not exactly what they expect according to theoretical probability and that they seldom get identical results when they repeat an experiment. The experiments students conduct lead to some questions that get to the heart of the difference between theoretical and experimental probability (e.g., if a coin has a $\frac{1}{2}$ chance of turning up heads on a single flip, why doesn't it turn up heads exactly half the time?). See **Teacher Note:** Impossible, Certain, and Everything in Between, page 134.

## This Unit also focuses on

◆ Using U.S. standard units to measure lengths longer than the measuring tool

## Ten-Minute Math activities focus on

◆ Describing features of the data

◆ Interpreting and posing questions about the data

◆ Generating equivalent expressions for a number using particular constraints

◆ Practicing computation skills

◆ Using notation to record expressions

**LOOKING FORWARD** During the rest of this year, students will continue working on collecting, representing, and describing data in the Ten-Minute Math activity *Quick Survey.* This activity occurs in two of the subsequent units, *Fraction Cards and Decimal Squares and Penny Jars and Plant Growth.* This activity provides the opportunity for students to see a variety of data sets and to continue to develop their skills in interpreting data representations and describing a data set as a whole. In Grade 5, students focus on collecting and analyzing data from experiments. They also continue their work on using fractions and decimals to measure probability, and they work on probability problems involving fair and unfair games.

Getting Started with the *LogoPaths* Software   Students are formally introduced to the *LogoPaths* software in the 2-D Geometry and Measurement unit *Size, Shape, and Symmetry,* the fourth unit in the Grade 4 sequence. However, if you plan to use the software this year, we recommend that students have access to the software **outside of math time** starting with this unit in order to return to *Feed the Turtle,* a *LogoPaths* activity from Grade 3, and to spend time with the *Free Explore* option. For information about the *LogoPaths* software and directions for *Feed the Turtle,* refer to the *Software Support Reference Guide* found on the CD. See **Part 5: Technology in Investigations: Calculators and Computers** in *Implementing Investigations in Grade 4:* Introducing and Managing the *LogoPaths* software in Grade 4.

# Assessment

## IN THIS UNIT

### ONGOING ASSESSMENT: Observing Students at Work

The following sessions provide **Ongoing Assessment: Observing Students at Work** opportunities:

- **Session 1.1, p. 27**
- **Session 1.2, p. 33**
- **Session 1.3, pp. 38 and 40**
- **Session 1.4, p. 42**
- **Session 1.5, p. 48**
- **Session 2.1, p. 60**

- **Session 2.2, pp. 64, 65, and 66**
- **Session 2.3, p. 70**
- **Session 2.4, p. 73**
- **Session 2.5, p. 78**
- **Session 2.6, p. 85**

- **Session 2.7, p. 88**
- **Session 3.1, p. 99**
- **Session 3.2, p. 105**
- **Session 3.3, p. 111**
- **Session 3.4, p. 115**

### WRITING OPPORTUNITIES

The following sessions have **writing** opportunities for students to explain their mathematical thinking:

- **Session 1.4, p. 42**
  *Student Activity Book*, p. 7

- **Session 2.1, pp. 58–59**
  *Student Activity Book*, pp. 10–12

- **Session 2.4, p. 72**
  *Student Activity Book*, p. 20

- **Session 2.5, pp. 76–77**
  *Student Activity Book*, pp. 25–27

- **Session 3.2, p. 105**
  *Student Activity Book*, pp. 43–44

### PORTFOLIO OPPORTUNITIES

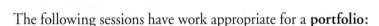

The following sessions have work appropriate for a **portfolio:**

- **Session 1.4, p. 42**
  *Student Activity Book*, p. 7

- **Session 1.5, p. 49**
  M7–M8, Assessment: Comparing
  Number of Cavities

- **Session 2.7, pp. 88–89**
  *Student Activity Book*, pp. 34–35

- **Session 3.4, p. 114**
  *Student Activity Book*, pp. 49–50

- **Session 3.5, pp. 118–119**
  M18–M21, End-of-Unit Assessment

# Assessing the Benchmarks

Observing students as they engage in conversation about their ideas is a primary means to assess their mathematical understanding. Consider all of your students' work, not just the written assessments. See the chart below for suggestions about key activities to observe.

 Checklist Available

| Benchmarks in This Unit | Key Activities to Observe | Assessment |
|---|---|---|
| 1. Design an effective survey question to compare two groups. | **Session 2.1:** Choosing and Revising a Survey Question | |
| 2. Organize and represent data about two groups in order to compare the groups. | **Session 1.3:** Representing the Heights of Fourth and First Graders<br><br>**Session 2.3:** Representing Data from Two Groups | **Session 2.2 Assessment Activity:**<br>Collecting and Comparing Data ✓ |
| 3. Describe the shape of the data from a numerical data set, including where the data are concentrated and the highest, lowest, and median values. | **Session 1.4:** Comparing the Heights of Fourth and First Graders<br><br>**Session 2.6:** Comparing WNBA Players' Points Per Game | **Session 1.5 Assessment Activity:** Comparing Numbers of Cavities<br><br>**Session 3.5 End-of-Unit Assessment:** Problem 2A |
| 4. Use data to compare two groups. | **Session 1.4:** Comparing the Heights of Fourth and First Graders<br><br>**Session 2.6:** Comparing WNBA Players' Points Per Game | **Session 1.5 Assessment Activity:** Comparing Numbers of Cavities<br><br>**Session 3.5 End-of-Unit Assessment:** Problems 2B, 2C, and 2D |
| 5. Use evidence from a set of data to support an argument. | **Session 2.4:** Analyzing Data<br>**Session 2.7:** Is This a Good Game? | **Session 3.5 End-of-Unit Assessment:** Problems 2B, 2C, and 2D |
| 6. Describe the likelihood of an event in terms of a scale from impossible (probability of 0) to certain (probability of 1). | **Session 3.2:** Placing Events on a Likelihood Line | **Session 3.5 End-of-Unit Assessment:** Problems 1A, 1B, and 1C |

# Relating the Mathematical Emphases to the Benchmarks

| Mathematical Emphases | Benchmarks |
|---|---|
| **Data Analysis** Representing data | 2 |
| **Data Analysis** Describing, summarizing, and comparing data | 3 and 4 |
| **Data Analysis** Analyzing and interpreting data | 5 |
| **Data Analysis** Designing and carrying out a data investigation | 1 |
| **Probability** Describing the probability of an event | 6 |

# Ten-Minute Math

## IN THIS UNIT

**Ten-Minute Math** offers practice and review of key concepts for this grade level. These daily activities, to be done in ten minutes outside of math class, are introduced in a unit and repeated throughout the grade. Specific directions for the day's activity are provided in each session. For the full description and variations of each classroom activity, see *Implementing Investigations in Grade 4*.

| Activity | Introduced | Full Description of Activity and Its Variations |
|---|---|---|
| *Today's Number* | Session 1.1 (this unit) | *Implementing Investigations in Grade 4* |
| *Quick Survey* | Session 1.4 (this unit) | *Implementing Investigations in Grade 4* |

## Today's Number

Students write several different addition and subtraction expressions that equal a given number. They are given constraints, in the context of broken calculator keys, that define the operations and the numbers they can use. Students practice and develop flexibility with computation skills.

### Math Focus Points

◆ Generating equivalent expressions for a number using particular constraints

◆ Practicing computation skills

◆ Using notation to record expressions

## Quick Survey

Students collect, display, describe, and interpret data about themselves or something they can observe easily. Students describe what they can tell from the data, generate some new questions and, if appropriate, make predictions about what will happen the next time they collect the same data.

### Math Focus Points

◆ Describing features of the data

◆ Interpreting and posing questions about the data

# Practice and Review

Practice and review play a critical role in the *Investigations* program. The following components and features are available to provide regular reinforcement of key mathematical concepts and procedures.

| Books | Features | In This Unit . . . |
|---|---|---|
| **Curriculum Unit** | **Ten-Minute Math** offers practice and review of key concepts for this grade level. These daily activities, to be done in ten minutes outside of math class, are introduced in a unit and repeated throughout the grade. Specific directions for the day's activity are provided in each session. For the full description and variations of each classroom activity, see *Implementing Investigations in Grade 4*. | • **All sessions** |
| **Student Activity Book** | **Daily Practice** pages in the *Student Activity Book* provide one of three types of written practice: **reinforcement** of the content of the unit, **ongoing review,** or **enrichment** opportunities. Some Daily Practice pages will also have Ongoing Review items with multiple-choice problems similar to those on standardized tests. | • **All sessions** |
| | **Homework** pages in the *Student Activity Book* are an extension of the work done in class. At times they help students prepare for upcoming activities. | • **Session 1.2**  • **Session 2.5** <br> • **Session 1.3**  • **Session 2.7** <br> • **Session 2.1**  • **Session 3.1** <br> • **Session 2.2**  • **Session 3.2** <br> • **Session 2.4** |
| **Student Math Handbook** | **Math Words and Ideas** in the *Student Math Handbook* are pages that summarize key words and ideas. Most Words and Ideas pages have at least one exercise. | • **Student Math Handbook, pp. 87–100** |
| | **Games** pages are found in a section of the *Student Math Handbook*. | • **No games are introduced in this unit.** |

# IN THIS UNIT

## Supporting the Range of Learners

| Sessions | 1.1 | 1.3 | 1.5 | 2.1 | 2.2 | 2.5 | 2.6 | 2.7 | 3.1 | 3.2 | 3.3 |
|---|---|---|---|---|---|---|---|---|---|---|---|
| Intervention | | • | | • | • | • | • | • | | • | • |
| Extension | | • | | | | • | | | | | • |
| ELL | • | | • | | | | | | • | | |

## Intervention

Suggestions are made to support and engage students who are having difficulty with a particular idea, activity, or problem.

## Extension

Suggestions are made to support and engage students who finish early or may be ready for additional challenge.

## English Language Learners (ELL)

In this unit, students must learn how to collect, represent, describe, and compare data. They must also be able to discuss the likelihood of an event both numerically and in words. As they work through the material, English Language Learners will need to learn a great deal of everyday vocabulary in addition to relevant mathematical terms. For this reason, it will be useful to preview some of the activities and vocabulary necessary to describe amounts of data. English Language Learners will then be better prepared to participate in class discussions in which expressions such as *different, highest, lowest, clumps, most, spread out,* and *close together* are used.

You can also review some of the lessons to reinforce key vocabulary as well as to assess English Language Learners' understanding of the concepts covered. When processing this new vocabulary, English Language Learners may lose sight of the information that the numbers represent. After establishing an understanding of the mathematical terms, you will need to continue reviewing the significance of the data.

*Working with the Range of Learners: Classroom Cases* is a set of episodes written by teachers that focuses on meeting the needs of the range of learners in the classroom. In the first section, *Setting up the Mathematical Community,* teachers write about how they create a supportive and productive learning environment in their classrooms. In the next section, *Accommodations for Learning,* teachers focus on specific modifications they make to meet the needs of some of their learners. In the last section, *Language and Representation,* teachers share how they help students use representations and develop language to investigate and express mathematical ideas. The questions at the end of each case provide a starting point for your own reflection or for discussion with colleagues. See *Implementing Investigations in Grade 4* for this set of episodes.

## Mathematical Emphases

### Data Analysis Representing data

### Math Focus Points

◆ Organizing ordered numerical data to describe a data set

◆ Using a line plot to represent ordered numerical data

◆ Representing two sets of data in order to compare them

### Data Analysis Describing, summarizing, and comparing data

### Math Focus Points

◆ Describing the shape of a data set: where the data are spread out or concentrated, what the highest and lowest values are, what the range is, and what the outliers are

◆ Describing what values are typical or atypical in a data set

◆ Determining the range of a data set

◆ Describing and interpreting data that compare two groups

◆ Finding the median of a data set

◆ Using medians to compare groups

◆ Considering what information a median does and does not provide

### Data Analysis Analyzing and interpreting data

### Math Focus Points

◆ Developing arguments based on data

### Data Analysis Designing and carrying out a data investigation

### Math Focus Points

◆ Recording and keeping track of data

◆ Considering how well a data representation communicates to an audience

### This Investigation also focuses on

◆ Using U.S. standard units to measure lengths longer than the measuring tool

# Landmarks in the Data

| | Student Activity Book | Student Math Handbook | Professional Development: Read Ahead of Time | |
|---|---|---|---|---|
| **SESSION 1.1**     p. 22 | | | | |
| **How Many Raisins in a Box?** Students record and organize data about the number of raisins in a box and describe the shape of the data distribution. | 1 | 88–89 | • **Mathematics in This Unit,** p. 10<br>• **Part 4: Ten-Minute Math** in *Implementing Investigations in Grade 4:* Today's Number<br>• **Teacher Notes:** Data Terms and Representations, p. 121; Focusing on the Shape of the Data, p. 123<br>• **Dialogue Box:** Describing the Shape of the Raisin Data, p. 144 | |
| **SESSION 1.2**     p. 30 | | | | |
| **How Tall Are Fourth Graders?** Students measure the heights of their classmates and use the data to describe the heights of students in the class. | 2–3 | 90–91 | • **Dialogue Box:** What Is a Typical Height?, p. 146 | |
| **SESSION 1.3**     p. 36 | | | | |
| **How Tall Are First Graders?** Students collect height data from a first-grade class. They create a representation of first-grade and fourth-grade height data in order to compare the groups. | 5–6 | 94, 95, 96 | | |
| **SESSION 1.4**     p. 41 | | | | |
| **Comparing the Heights of Fourth and First Graders** Students use the representations they created to compare the heights of students in their own class with the heights of students in a first-grade class. | 7–8 | 94–97 | • **Part 4: Ten-Minute Math** in *Implementing Investigations in Grade 4:* Quick Survey | |
| **SESSION 1.5**     p. 46 | | | | |
| **Assessment: Comparing Numbers of Cavities** Students find and compare the medians of the fourth-grade heights and first-grade heights. Students complete an assessment in which they compare two data sets. | 9 | 92–93 | • **Teacher Note:** Finding and Using the Median, p. 125; Assessment: Comparing the Numbers of Cavities, p. 127<br>• **Dialogue Box:** What Does the Median Tell You?, p. 147 | |

| Materials to Gather | Materials to Prepare |
|---|---|
| • **Half-ounce boxes of raisins** (1 per student)<br>• **Calculators** | • **M1–M2, Family Letter**  Make copies. (1 per student) |
| • **Yardsticks or tape measures in inches** (at least 1 yardstick per 3 students)<br>• **Paper for marking heights** (optional) | • **M3–M4, Family Letter**  Make copies.<br>• **Chart paper**  Label one sheet "Measuring Suggestions." Label another sheet "Our Class Heights." Divide it into columns: Name and Height. Make sure that there is room for everyone's name. You may want to make four columns, two for names and two for heights. |
| • **Chart: "Measuring Suggestions"** (from Session 1.2)<br>• **Yardsticks or tape measures in inches** (at least 1 per pair)<br>• **Chart paper**<br>• **11″ x 17″ paper** (1 sheet per pair)<br>• **Markers or crayons** (as needed) | • **M6, Centimeter Grid Paper**  Make copies. Have available throughout this unit.<br>• **First-grade class list, or M5, Height Data from a First Grade Class**  Make copies. (1 per pair)<br>• **First-grade data**  Arrange with the first-grade teacher(s) for your students to collect the heights of first graders. You may need to arrange for students to collect the data of the first-graders' heights outside math time.<br>• **Chart paper**  Label the chart "Heights of First Graders." Divide it into columns: Name and Height. Make sure that there is room for everyone's name.<br>• **Our Class Heights list**  Write the height data from Session 1.2 on a sheet of paper. You do not have to include the names. Make copies. (1 per pair) |
| • **Materials for making representations** (from Session 1.3)<br>• **Chart paper** (optional) | |
| • **Representations of first and fourth graders' heights** (from Session 1.4)<br>• **Our Class Heights list** (1 per pair; from Session 1.3)<br>• **Heights of First Graders list** (1 per pair; from Session 1.3) | • **M7–M8, Assessment: Comparing Numbers of Cavities**  Make copies. (1 per student)<br>• **Cavity data for the class**  Collate the cavity data from Session 1.3 homework, *Student Activity Book* page 6, into a list and make copies. Alternatively, use Cavity Data from a Fourth-Grade Class (M9) and make copies. (1 per student) |

# How Many Raisins in a Box?

## Math Focus Points

- Organizing ordered, numerical data to describe a data set
- Describing the shape of a data set: where the data are spread out or concentrated, what the highest and lowest values are, what the range is, and what the outliers are
- Describing what values are typical or atypical in a data set

### Vocabulary

**data**
**bar graph**
**line plot**

| Today's Plan | | Materials |
|---|---|---|
| **ACTIVITY** ① **Introducing** *Today's Number:* *Broken Calculator* | 15 MIN   CLASS | • Calculators |
| **ACTIVITY** ② **Representing the Number of Raisins in a Box** | 30 MIN   CLASS   PAIRS | • Half-ounce boxes of raisins |
| **DISCUSSION** ③ **Describing the Raisin Data** | 15 MIN   CLASS | |
| **SESSION FOLLOW-UP** ④ **Daily Practice** | | • *Student Activity Book,* p. 1 <br> • *Student Math Handbook,* pp. 88–89 <br> • M1–M2, Family Letter* |

*See *Materials to Prepare,* p. 21.

## Ten-Minute Math

*Today's Number: Broken Calculator*  Students write five expressions that equal 2,400. They must use either subtraction or addition in their expressions. The 2 and 4 keys are broken. Have two or three students give their answers as equations and explain why they are correct. ($3,000 - 600 = 2,400$ or $1,563 + 837 = 2,400$)

**ACTIVITY**

# Introducing *Today's Number: Broken Calculator*

15 MIN    CLASS

Introduce students to the Ten-Minute Math activity, *Today's Number: Broken Calculator.*❶ They will be doing this activity outside math class throughout this unit. In the basic *Today's Number* activity, which students may remember from Grade 3, students write equations for a given number by using any operation or combination of operations that they choose. In the *Broken Calculator* variation, students create expressions on a calculator and are told to imagine that one or more keys on the calculator are "broken" and therefore cannot be used.❷

Today's number is 364. On your calculator, find some ways to make the display read 364, using only addition. You may add more than two numbers together if you want to.

Give students a minute or two to generate several expressions, and then collect a few solutions. Write these as equations on the board. They may include the following:

$$300 + 60 + 4 = 364$$
$$360 + 4 = 364$$
$$200 + 150 + 14 = 364$$
$$363 + 1 = 364$$

Now imagine this: Your calculator is broken, and some of the keys don't work. Let's say that the 3 key and the 4 key are broken. How could you make the calculator read 364, without using the 3 or 4 keys? This time, you may use either addition or subtraction.

**Professional Development**

❶ **Ten-Minute Math** in *Implementing Investigations in Grade 4*: **Today's Number**

**Differentiation**

❷ **English Language Learners** It may be difficult for English Language Learners to follow the directions for this activity. You can preview it with them to be sure they understand the basic premise and, if necessary, to show them how to use a calculator. You can also establish a written pattern that you will follow each time you give the directions to the class so English Language Learners can more easily participate. **First, I'll write the number you want to reach, like 364. Under the number, I'll write the symbol or symbols you can use, like + or −. Then, under the symbols, I'll write the numbers that are "broken," that you cannot use, with an "x" through them, like this:**

364
+
3̶ 4̶

After English Language Learners have done the activity several times, check to see if they can follow the instructions without the written support.

Give students another minute or two to work on this problem, and then collect several solutions. Write these as equations on the board. They may include the following:

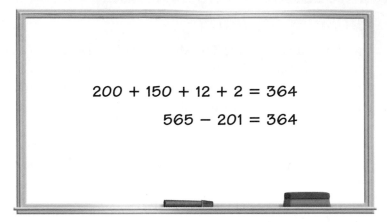

$$200 + 150 + 12 + 2 = 364$$
$$565 - 201 = 364$$

Ask a few students to talk about how they came up with their solutions.

**Students might say:**

"First I did 365 minus 1, but I had to use the 3 key. I couldn't do 465 minus 101 either, because that used the 4 key, so I made it 565 minus 201."

Can you find a way to combine addition and subtraction in your solution? Remember, the 3 and 4 keys are still broken.

Students' solutions may include:

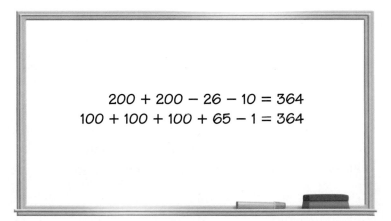

$$200 + 200 - 26 - 10 = 364$$
$$100 + 100 + 100 + 65 - 1 = 364$$

Choose one or two of the solutions you collect to talk about with the class. Let students know that they will be doing more *Broken Calculator* problems throughout the unit for Ten-Minute Math.

ACTIVITY

30 MIN   CLASS   PAIRS

# 2 Representing the Number of Raisins in a Box

Briefly introduce this new unit to your class.

In this unit we will be collecting, representing, and describing data. People collect data to gather information they want to know about the world around them.

Students may be familiar with data collected about academic tests, sports, health issues such as smoking, or other data reported in the newspaper or on TV.

If possible, give students an example of the use of data from your own school or community. For example, in one school a principal found that students were getting injured on a particular piece of playground equipment. After examining data about the injuries, the principal noticed that mostly younger students were getting injured. He eventually concluded that younger students did not have big enough hands to grasp the bars securely. As a result, only students in Grade 4 or older were allowed to use the equipment.

Can you think of any other ways people might use data?

Have two or three students share examples.

In this first activity, students collect data on the number of raisins in a box. The emphasis is on ways to organize and represent data in order to gather information easily from the representation.

Just like mathematicians and scientists who use data, we can collect data to find out information about ourselves or the world around us. Today, we are going to start by collecting data about something familiar—a box of raisins.

Give each student a box of raisins. Ask them to open their boxes and predict how many raisins might be in their box. Then ask them to count the raisins.

Have students report their data as they finish their counts. Record the numbers in a list on the board, in whatever order they are reported.

What do you notice about the data we collected about the number of raisins in a box?

**Professional Development**

❸ **Teacher Note:** Data Terms and Representations, p. 121

We can notice some things about these data by looking at this list, but we could probably notice more if we organize the data better. What could we do to organize the data so that you can say more about how many raisins are in a box?

Take a few suggestions from students. Then give them about 10 minutes to work in pairs. Have each pair choose a way to organize the data. Emphasize that they should find a quick way to represent the data—a rough sketch or list, for example, not an elaborate graph. After students have organized the data, each pair should write one or two important things they can say about the data.

Choose two or three pairs of students who have used different ways of ordering and organizing the data to put sketches of their representations on the board or overhead. For example, you might choose an ordered list, a bar graph, and a line plot.

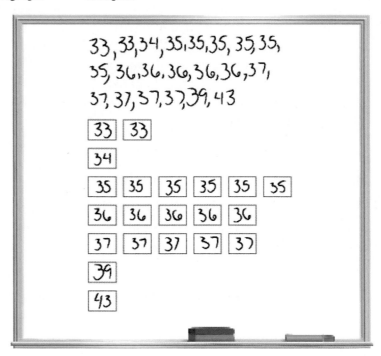

When you reconvene the class, ask what each representation helped students notice about the data.

Before, we had the number of raisins in your boxes listed in the order you reported them. What did [Amelia] and [Enrique] do in their representation that helps us describe the whole set of data? What did [Yuki] and [Kimberly] do?

Review the line plot as a useful way of organizing data. If some students used a line plot, refer to their work as you organize the raisin data on a line plot.❸

Have students report data to help you draw the line plot. First, ask them to give the lowest and highest values so that you can draw a horizontal line and mark it with the relevant values. Then ask a student to read off the data from the original unorganized list as you represent each piece of data with an X over the appropriate number. Label the line plot "Number of Raisins in a Half-Ounce Box."

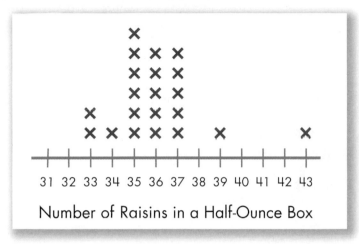

Let students know that this is one useful way of representing data.

In our work in this unit, you will be representing data so that you can better describe what the data show. A line plot—which many of you remember from Grade 3—is one kind of representation that is useful. You will probably find other ways of representing data during this unit that work well, too. As we talk about what you noticed about the raisin data, keep thinking about how your own representation and your classmates' representations help you see the data more clearly.

## ONGOING ASSESSMENT: Observing Students at Work

Students make a quick representation of a data set and write what they notice about the data.

- **Can students organize the data?** Do they order or group the data by value?

- **Can students describe the shape of the data?** What aspects do they describe?

- **Are students familiar with a line plot as a data representation?**

As you watch students work, use this opportunity to get a sense of what your class knows about organizing and representing numerical data.

## Teaching Note

❹ **Describing Data** Make sure that students clearly relate each statement to what it tells them about the number of raisins in a box. When students talk only about the numbers or symbols they see on a representation, they sometimes lose their sense of what those numbers or symbols mean. Even if the student who makes the statement knows what each number refers to, other students may not.

## Professional Development

❺ **Dialogue Box:** Describing the Shape of the Raisin Data, p. 144

## Math Note

❻ **Looking at the Values** Many students at first notice the mode and may focus only on that value as important. Support students in establishing a clump of values that could be considered typical or usual.

---

### DISCUSSION

# ③ Describing the Raisin Data

15 MIN   CLASS

## Math Focus Points for Discussion

◆ Describing the shape of a data set: where the data are spread out or concentrated, what the highest and lowest values are, what the range is, and what the outliers are

◆ Describing what values are typical or atypical in a data set

Ask students to share the statements they wrote about the data. ❹

### Students might say:

"There's 5 on 37."

"That tells us that 5 boxes had 37 raisins in them."

After a few students have shared what they noticed, focus the students on the overall shape of the data by asking some of the following questions: ❺

* What is the highest number of raisins in a box? What is the lowest number? So, the number of raisins in a box ranges from [33] to [43].

* Are the data showing the number of raisins in a box spread out or close together?

* Where is there a great deal of data?

* Are there any outliers—pieces of data that are far away from the other pieces of data?

Finish the discussion by focusing on summarizing what the data show. ❻

* Suppose that someone asked you, "About how many raisins are in a half-ounce box?" What would you say? Why?

* What's a fairly typical number of raisins in a box, according to our data?

* If you opened more boxes of raisins, what would you expect?

* What would be an unusual number of raisins to find in a box?

Student comments might include, "I wouldn't be surprised to get between 35 and 37 raisins," or "I'd be really surprised to get over 40."

Encourage students to quantify the data that they see in the "typical or usual" clump.

So how many of our boxes had between [35] and [37] raisins? Is that more or less than half the class?❼

## DIFFERENTIATION: Supporting the Range of Learners

**ELL** After the class discussion, you can assess whether English Language Learners understand the significance of the data by asking them a few questions. Begin by defining the words *typical* and *atypical*. Then ask questions such as

- Are there more boxes with 32 raisins or with 42 raisins? Is 36 a typical amount or an atypical amount?

After thoroughly reviewing the data, take an unopened box of raisins and ask

- How many raisins do you think are in this box?

If students do not suggest a number that makes sense from the data, you can point at the relevant points on the line plot to help them use the range to make their guess. Finally, have students count the actual number of raisins in the box to see how close they were to the correct number, and ask them to show you where this number would fit into the data and line plot.

## SESSION FOLLOW-UP

# 4 Daily Practice

 **Daily Practice:** For ongoing review, have students complete *Student Activity Book* page 1.

 **Student Math Handbook:** Students and families may use *Student Math Handbook* pages 88–89 for reference and review. See pages 154–157 in the back of this unit.

 **Family Letter:** Send home copies of the Family Letter (M1–M2).

❼ **Teacher Note:** Focusing on the Shape of the Data, p. 123

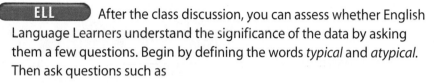

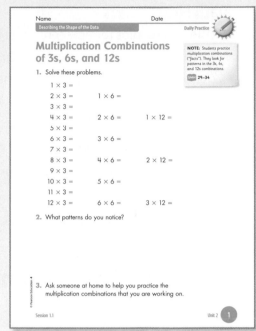

▲ **Student Activity Book, p. 1**

# How Tall Are Fourth Graders?

## Math Focus Points

- Using a line plot to represent ordered numerical data
- Describing the shape of a set of data: where the data are spread out or concentrated, what the highest and lowest values are, what the range is, and what the outliers are
- Determining the range of a data set
- Describing what values are typical or atypical in a data set
- Using U.S. standard units to measure lengths longer than the measuring tool

### Vocabulary

**outlier**

**range**

## Today's Plan

| Today's Plan | | Materials |
|---|---|---|
| **ACTIVITY** **①Measuring Heights in This Class** | 30 MIN GROUPS | • Yardsticks or tape measure in inches; paper for marking heights (optional); chart paper* |
| **DISCUSSION** **②Describing the Class Height Data** | 20 MIN CLASS | |
| **ACTIVITY** **③Introducing Predictions About First Graders' Heights** | 10 MIN CLASS | • Chart paper |
| **SESSION FOLLOW-UP** **④Daily Practice and Homework** | | • *Student Activity Book,* pp. 2–3 • *Student Math Handbook,* pp. 90–91 • M3–M4, Family Letter* |

*See *Materials to Prepare,* p. 21.

## Ten-Minute Math

***Today's Number: Broken Calculator***  Students create five expressions that equal 3,200. They must use either addition or subtraction in their expressions. The 2 and 3 keys are broken. Have two or three students give their answers as equations and explain why they are correct.

(Examples: 1,700 + 1,500 = 3,200 or 4,698 − 1,000 − 454 − 44 = 3,200)

For more details, see pages 23–24, as well as the full write-up for this activity in *Implementing Investigations in Grade 4.*

**ACTIVITY**

# 1 Measuring Heights in This Class

**30 MIN** **GROUPS**

This activity is the beginning of a project in which students work on the problem: How much taller is a fourth grader than a first grader? Introduce to your class the importance of using data to compare groups.

Sometimes we collect data in order to compare one group with another. For example, we could use your raisin data and compare them with a different brand of raisins or compare them with data collected by other people.

During the next few days, we are going to start working on a problem that involves comparing two sets of data. The problem is this: How much taller is a fourth grader than a first grader? First, we'll collect data about your heights; then, we'll plan the rest of the Investigation.

Show students the yardsticks or tape measures for them to use to measure one another's heights. Review these measurement tools and their units of measure, as needed.❶

Ask some of the following questions:

- How do you measure someone's height?

- We're going to be measuring in inches. If you start with a yardstick, how many inches is that?

- How would you continue measuring?

- How would you find out the total number of inches?

Issues that may come up include the following:

- Should students keep their shoes on?

- Does it help to stand with your back against a wall?

- How do you use the yardstick to measure a height that is longer than the yardstick?

Ask two students to demonstrate how they would measure each other.❷ Take suggestions from the class to help them. Then ask:

What do you need to pay attention to as you measure to make sure that you are measuring accurately? What do we need to decide as a group to make our measurements as consistent as possible?

Write students' suggestions on the chart paper labeled "Measuring Suggestions." Add other suggestions after students have measured one another.

Have students work in groups of three to measure their heights in inches. One student is measured, one student does the measuring, and the third checks the accuracy of the measurement and records it.❸

*Students work together to measure height.*

Students list each height on the chart labeled "Our Class Heights." You will need a complete list of heights for the discussion that follows.

Take this opportunity to informally assess what students understand about tools and units for measuring length. If some students are not measuring carefully or accurately, ask them to explain to you how they are measuring. Ask them about problems that affect the accuracy of their measurements.

I notice that sometimes you put your yardsticks end to end and sometimes you don't. Do you think that will make a difference in how accurate your measurements are?

## ONGOING ASSESSMENT: Observing Students at Work

Students measure and record one another's heights.

- **Do students measure carefully, trying to be as accurate as possible?** Do they use their measuring tools correctly?

- **Do they know how to use their measuring tools to measure something longer than the measuring tool?** How do students figure out the total number of inches for each student's height?

### Teaching Note

❹ **Save the Height Data** Make sure that you save the Grade 4 height data. Each student needs a copy of these data for the next session.

DISCUSSION

# ② Describing the Class Height Data

**20 MIN    CLASS**

## Math Focus Points for Discussion

◆ Describing the shape of a set of data: where the data are spread out or concentrated, what the highest and lowest values are, what the range is, and what the outliers are.

◆ Describing what values are typical or atypical in a data set

Make a line plot of the data, with the class's help, as you did with the raisin data.❹ Ask students to tell you what the minimum and maximum values are so that you can set up the scale for the line plot. A student can then read values off the list, or you can ask each student to report his or her height. Place an X over the appropriate point for each student's height. Here is an example of a finished plot.

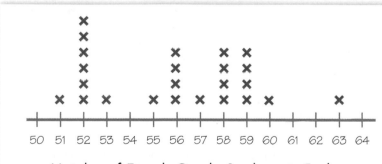

Heights of Fourth Grade Students in Inches

Ask students to describe the data.

Now that the data are organized, what can you say about how tall students are in our class?

**Math Note**

❺ **Fractions** Throughout this unit, help students use their knowledge of fractions as they describe data. Say, for example, "More than half the class has heights from 56 to 59 inches," or "About a third of us are shorter than 54 inches."

**Teaching Note**

❻ **Vocabulary** As data terms are brought up by you and by students, write them on a list where students can see them throughout the unit. Students often mishear these unfamiliar words, assuming they are the same as words they know. For example, students have thought that *mode* is *mold* and that *outlier* is spelled *outliar*.

**Professional Development**

❼ **Dialogue Box:** What Is a Typical Height?, p. 146

As students share their observations, help them focus on what the data show about the height of students in the class.❺ Use questions similar to those you used in the discussion about the raisin data:

- **What is the tallest height in our class? What is the shortest height in our class? So, the range of heights in our class is from [51] inches to [63] inches.**

- **Are the data showing your heights spread out or close together?**

- **Where is there a great deal of data?**

- **Where are there few data?**

- **Some people said that there is a clump of data between [56] and [59]. About how much of our class is in that clump? For example, are about half the people in the class in that clump? Or is it more or less than half our class?**

- **Are there any outliers—pieces of data that are far away from the other pieces of data?**

End the discussion by focusing on summarizing what the data show.

Suppose that someone asked you, "About how tall are fourth graders in your class?" What would you say? Why? What's a fairly typical height for our class? From our data, what would you expect if you measured the heights of more classes of fourth graders? What heights would not surprise you? What would be a height that you think you might find sometimes, but not often?❻

Some students may point to the mode as the typical height in the class. Others may describe a clump where data are concentrated. Others may talk about a middle value or a clump of data around a middle value. Encourage students not to focus on only one value but to look at larger clumps of data. For example, you might say:

[Marisol] and [Jake] were noticing that [6] of you have heights of [52] inches. That peak at [52] inches does stand out. But if we're telling someone what heights they might expect to see in a fourth-grade class, according to what we know about our own data, we should also remember that's only [6] of us, and that we have [24] students in our class. Is there a statement you can make about more of the class? Can anyone finish a sentence that starts, "More than half our class . . ." or "About half our class . . ."?❼

## ACTIVITY

10 MIN  CLASS

# Introducing Predictions About First-Graders' Heights

Remind students that they will be working on the question: How much taller is a fourth grader than a first grader? Tell them about the arrangements you have made for measuring first graders' heights. (See page 21 for information about making these arrangements.)

Then ask them to make some predictions about what they will find out.

*What do you think we will find out about the heights of first graders? How do you think they will be different from ours? How might they be similar? Could any first graders be the same height as a fourth grader, or will they all be shorter?*

Ask students whether they think the range of the first-grade data will be similar to the range for fourth-grade data.

*Our shortest height is [51] inches; our tallest height is [63] inches. How many inches from the lowest to highest value? So the range of our data is [12] inches—that's the difference between the shortest and tallest measurement. Do you think the first graders will have that kind of range? Do you think the shortest first grader will be [12] inches shorter than the tallest first grader?*

## SESSION FOLLOW-UP

# Daily Practice and Homework

 **Daily Practice:** For ongoing review, have students complete *Student Activity Book* page 2.

 **Homework:** Students solve a set of related multiplication combinations on *Student Activity Book* page 3.

 **Student Math Handbook:** Students and families may use *Student Math Handbook* pages 90–91 for reference and review. See pages 154–157 in the back of this unit.

 **Family Letter:** Send home copies of the Family Letter (M3–M4).

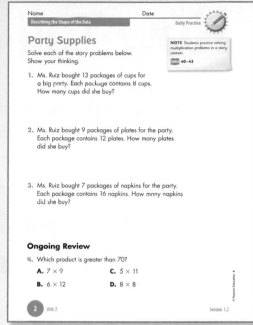

Name _____ Date _____
Describing the Shape of the Data                    Daily Practice

### Party Supplies

Solve each of the story problems below. Show your thinking.

NOTE Students practice solving multiplication problems in a story context.
40–43

1. Ms. Ruiz bought 13 packages of cups for a big party. Each package contains 8 cups. How many cups did she buy?

2. Ms. Ruiz bought 9 packages of plates for the party. Each package contains 12 plates. How many plates did she buy?

3. Ms. Ruiz bought 7 packages of napkins for the party. Each package contains 16 napkins. How many napkins did she buy?

**Ongoing Review**

4. Which product is greater than 70?

A. $7 \times 9$     C. $5 \times 11$

B. $6 \times 12$     D. $8 \times 8$

2  Unit 2                                    Session 1.2

▲ **Student Activity Book, p. 2**

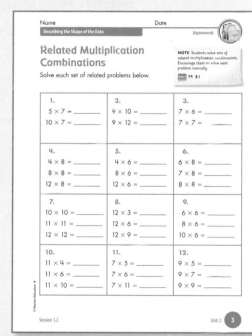

Name _____ Date _____
Describing the Shape of the Data                    Homework

### Related Multiplication Combinations

Solve each set of related problems below.

NOTE Students solve sets of related multiplication combinations. Encourage them to solve each problem mentally.

| 1. | 2. | 3. |
|---|---|---|
| $5 \times 7 =$ ___ | $9 \times 10 =$ ___ | $7 \times 6 =$ ___ |
| $10 \times 7 =$ ___ | $9 \times 12 =$ ___ | $7 \times 7 =$ ___ |
| **4.** | **5.** | **6.** |
| $4 \times 8 =$ ___ | $4 \times 6 =$ ___ | $6 \times 8 =$ ___ |
| $8 \times 8 =$ ___ | $8 \times 6 =$ ___ | $7 \times 8 =$ ___ |
| $12 \times 8 =$ ___ | $12 \times 6 =$ ___ | $8 \times 8 =$ ___ |
| **7.** | **8.** | **9.** |
| $10 \times 10 =$ ___ | $12 \times 3 =$ ___ | $6 \times 6 =$ ___ |
| $11 \times 11 =$ ___ | $12 \times 6 =$ ___ | $8 \times 6 =$ ___ |
| $12 \times 12 =$ ___ | $12 \times 9 =$ ___ | $10 \times 6 =$ ___ |
| **10.** | **11.** | **12.** |
| $11 \times 4 =$ ___ | $7 \times 5 =$ ___ | $9 \times 5 =$ ___ |
| $11 \times 6 =$ ___ | $7 \times 6 =$ ___ | $9 \times 7 =$ ___ |
| $11 \times 10 =$ ___ | $7 \times 11 =$ ___ | $9 \times 9 =$ ___ |

Session 1.2                                    Unit 2  3

▲ **Student Activity Book, p. 3**

# How Tall Are First Graders?

## Math Focus Points

◆ Recording and keeping track of data

◆ Representing two sets of data in order to compare them

◆ Considering how well a data representation communicates information to an audience

### Vocabulary

**data**

**representation**

| Today's Plan | | | | Materials |
|---|---|---|---|---|
| **ACTIVITY**<br>① **Measuring First-Graders' Heights** | 30 MIN | CLASS | PAIRS | • M5, or first-grade class list*; chart: "Measuring Suggestions" (from Session 1.2); yardsticks or tape measures in inches; chart paper* |
| **ACTIVITY**<br>② **Representing the Heights of First and Fourth Graders** | 30 MIN | PAIRS | | • M6 (optional)*<br>• Our Class Heights list*; Heights of First-Graders list (from Activity 1); 11" by 17" paper; markers or crayons |
| **SESSION FOLLOW-UP**<br>③ **Daily Practice and Homework** | | | | • *Student Activity Book*, pp. 5–6<br>• *Student Math Handbook*, pp. 94, 95, 96 |

*See *Materials to Prepare*, p. 21.

## Ten-Minute Math

***Today's Number: Broken Calculator*** Students create five expressions that equal 754. They must use both addition and subtraction in their expressions. The 7 key is broken. Have two or three students give their answers as equations and explain how they know they are correct. (Examples: $954 - 300 + 100 = 754$ or $432 + 330 - 8 = 754$)

### ACTIVITY

# Measuring First Graders' Heights

30 MIN | CLASS | PAIRS

Before students measure the heights of the first graders, ❶ ask them whether there are any problems that came up as they measured their own heights that should be added to your list of Measuring Suggestions.

As we discussed during the last session, today we are going to collect data on the heights of a class of first graders to help us with our question: How much taller is a fourth grader than a first grader? You are going to measure the heights of a class of first graders, just as you measured the heights of your classmates. Let's take a few minutes to think about what you have to pay attention to in order to measure the first graders' heights as accurately as possible. Is there anything else that came up while you were measuring your classmates that we could add to our list?

Hand out the copies of the class list for the first-grade class, and assign each pair to measure one or two first graders. Spend a few minutes discussing any other logistical information students may need, as well as how to be respectful of the first graders they are measuring.

*Students measure and record the heights of first graders.*

After your students have measured all of the first graders, gather the data they collected. Record the data on the "Heights of First Graders" chart. Help students copy the data onto their own class lists so that each student has a complete list of the heights of the first-grade class.

Name _____ Date _____

**Describing the Shape of the Data**

## Height Data from a First-Grade Class

If you are unable to arrange for your class to collect height data from a first-grade class, you can use the following data instead:

| Name | Height |
|------|--------|
| Allie | 50 inches |
| Bruce | 49 inches |
| Carol | 39 inches |
| Chris | 52 inches |
| Diego | 52 inches |
| Edgar | 49 inches |
| Emilia | 48 inches |
| Felipe | 45 inches |
| Isabel | 50 inches |
| Jacinta | 46 inches |
| Jacob | 52 inches |
| Leah | 54 inches |
| Libby | 50 inches |
| Lyle | 52 inches |
| Marta | 49 inches |
| Nicky | 48 inches |
| Paul | 47 inches |
| Paula | 46 inches |
| Seth | 50 inches |
| Talisa | 53 inches |
| Tamika | 48 inches |
| Teo | 47 inches |

Session 1.3                                    Unit 2  M5

▲ **Resource Masters, M5**

### Centimeter Grid Paper

Name

Date

Describing the Shape of the Data

M6  Unit 2                     Sessions 1.3, 1.4, 2.1, 2.2, 2.3, 3.3

© Pearson Education 4

▲ Resource Masters, M6

## ONGOING ASSESSMENT: Observing Students at Work

Students measure the heights of first graders.

- **Do students measure carefully, trying to be as accurate as possible?** Do they use their measuring tools correctly?

- **Do they know how to use their measuring tools to measure something longer than the measuring tool?** How do students figure out the total number of inches for each student's height?

**ACTIVITY**

30 MIN   PAIRS

# ② Representing the Heights of First and Fourth Graders

Introduce the task of making a representation to compare first-grade and fourth-grade heights.

You have collected data on our heights and the heights of a first-grade class. In order to try to figure out how much taller a fourth grader is than a first grader, you need to compare the two classes. Today, you are going to make a representation or representations of these two sets of data to help you compare them. What are some ways that you might represent these two sets of data so that they are easy to compare?

Ask students to talk to a person next to them about how they might represent these data sets so that they are easy to compare. Then ask three or four students to share their ideas with the whole class. Some representations may be difficult to describe verbally, so consider asking some students to quickly sketch their ideas. As students share their ideas, ask them how their representations might make it easy to compare both sets of data. You may want to remind them of the representations they created during Session 1.1 for the raisin data.

As you work on your representations, remember that [your parents, the principal, the teacher next door] will be seeing these. Try to make your representation clear so that someone who doesn't know about our project can understand what your representation shows.

Students work in pairs to represent and compare the first- and fourth-grade heights, using their lists of first-grade heights and of their class heights. They should first discuss possible ways to represent the data with their partner and then choose a way to represent the data. Provide copies of Centimeter Grid Paper (M6) as needed. Encourage students to sketch their ideas first before making a final copy on a large sheet of paper.

As they make their representations, they should double-check to make sure that they include all the data accurately. They can continue their work in the next session.

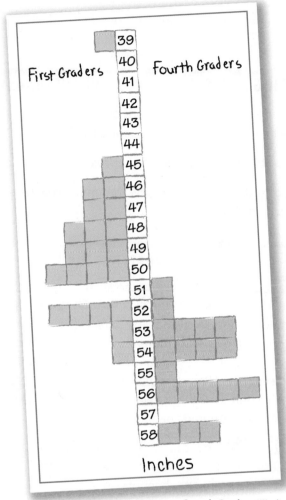

*Sample Student Work*

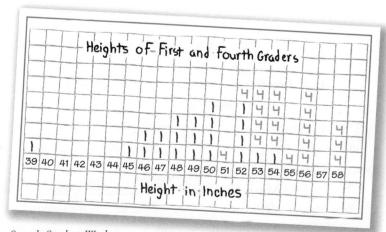

*Sample Student Work*

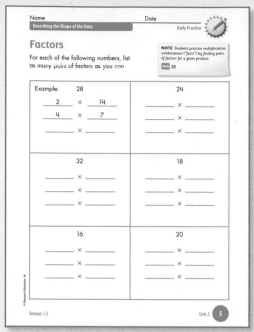

▲ **Student Activity Book, p. 5**

▲ **Student Activity Book, p. 6**

As students work, ask them how their representations will help them compare the data.

Can you easily see the first-grade data? The fourth-grade data?

What features of your representation help someone looking at it compare the two groups?

## ONGOING ASSESSMENT: Observing Students at Work

Students create representations of the fourth- and first-grade height data in order to compare the data sets.

- **Do students organize and represent the data clearly?**

- **Do students create graphs that make the data sets easy to compare?**

## DIFFERENTIATION: Supporting the Range of Learners

**Intervention** For students who are having trouble finding a way to organize and represent the data in order to compare groups, you might want to suggest a way that you think will work for them. Refer students back to their own ways of representing the raisin data. Can they use ideas from that representation? How would they improve on that representation? Remind them about the line plots of the raisin data from Session 1.1. Is there a way they can use a line plot to show the first- and fourth-grade data?

**Extension** Any students who complete their representations during this session can write a few statements about what they notice about the data on a separate sheet of paper.

**SESSION FOLLOW-UP**

# ③ Daily Practice and Homework

 **Daily Practice:** For ongoing review, have students complete *Student Activity Book* page 5.

 **Homework:** Students find out how many cavities they have had and record the amount on *Student Activity Book* page 6. They will use the data for an assessment in Session 1.5.

 **Student Math Handbook:** Students and families may use *Student Math Handbook* pages 94, 95, 96 for reference and review. See pages 154–157 in the back of this unit.

# Comparing the Heights of Fourth and First Graders

## Math Focus Points

◆ Describing and interpreting data that compare two groups

◆ Describing what values are typical or atypical in a data set

◆ Developing arguments based on data

| Today's Plan | | Materials |
|---|---|---|
| **ACTIVITY** **①** **Comparing the Heights of Fourth and First Graders** | 30 MIN · PAIRS | • *Student Activity Book,* p. 7<br>• Materials for making representations (from Session 1.3) |
| **DISCUSSION** **②** **How Much Taller Is a Fourth Grader?** | 30 MIN · CLASS | • Students' completed representations from Activity 1; chart paper (optional) |
| **SESSION FOLLOW-UP** **③** **Daily Practice** | | • *Student Activity Book,* p. 8<br>• *Student Math Handbook,* pp. 94–97 |

## Ten-Minute Math

Note: The Ten-Minute Math activity for this unit, *Quick Survey,* is not formally introduced, but students work on the mathematics from the unit. For a full description of the activity, see Part 4: Ten-Minute Math in *Implementing Investigations in Grade 4: Quick Survey.*

*Quick Survey* For the survey, ask the class "What is the largest number of pizza slices you have eaten?" or a different numerical question that you or the students choose. Make sure the data they collect is something they already know or can observe easily. With today's data, make a table. Ask the following:

• What do you notice about the data? What does the data tell us about our class?

Name _____ Date _____

Describing the Shape of the Data

**Comparing the Heights of First and Fourth Graders**

1. How do the heights of the first-graders compare with the heights of the fourth graders in your class? Write three statements about this question.

   In your statements include ideas about the data such as these: Where are there lots of data? How big are clumps of data? What are the tallest heights and the shortest heights? What outliers are there? What do you think are the typical heights of first graders and of fourth graders?

   a. _____
   b. _____
   c. _____

2. About how much taller do you think a fourth grader is than a first grader? Why do you think so? Support your ideas with evidence from the data.

   _____
   _____
   _____
   _____
   _____
   _____

Session 1.4                    Unit 2    7

▲ **Student Activity Book, p. 7**

**ACTIVITY**

**1** **Comparing the Heights of Fourth and First Graders**

30 MIN    PAIRS

Before students complete their representations, look together at *Student Activity Book* page 7. Tell students that there is not just one answer to Question 2 but that students should support their opinion with evidence from the data.

Students now finish their representations of the fourth-grade and first-grade height data that they began in Session 1.3. Then they analyze the data by answering the questions on *Student Activity Book* page 7.

*Students compare heights of first and fourth graders and draw conclusions about the data.*

**ONGOING ASSESSMENT: Observing Students at Work**

Students compare the heights of first graders and fourth graders by using the representations they created.

● **Do students create graphs that show the data clearly and make it easy to compare the two sets of data?**

● **Do students describe where the data are concentrated in their statements of comparison?** Do they notice how the range of each group is similar or different? Do they notice whether the data overlap? Do they notice any outliers in the data?

- **Do students draw some conclusions about how much taller a fourth grader is than a first grader?** Do they use evidence from the data to support their conclusions?

**DISCUSSION**

## How Much Taller Is a Fourth Grader?

30 MIN   CLASS

### Math Focus Points for Discussion

◆ Describing and interpreting data that compare two groups

◆ Developing arguments based on data

Have students post their representations of the height data around the room. Let students spend about five minutes looking at all the different representations done by the class. Ask them to consider why a particular representation helps them compare the two sets of data, and ask them to be ready to share specific examples.

If someone who didn't know anything about our project visited our classroom, how would these representations help that person compare the heights of first and fourth graders?

After five minutes, come together as a class.

You represented the first- and fourth-grade height data in different ways, but you all worked to find ways to make it easy to compare the two sets of data. What did you see in your classmates' representations that you think would help someone compare the first graders and fourth graders?

After students have had a chance to point out features of the representations, turn the discussion to their comparison statements.

What did you notice when you compared the heights from the first-grade class with our heights?❶

As the discussion continues, bring up specific aspects about the shape of the data that students have not brought up, using some of the following questions:

- How do the ranges of the heights compare between the two classes? Are the ranges about the same? Are there about the same number of inches between the shortest first grader and the tallest first grader as between the shortest fourth grader and the tallest fourth grader?

### Math Note

❶ **Describing Data**  As students share what they noticed when they compared the two groups, make sure they are making statements that relate to what the data represent rather than just referring to numbers. For example, if students are making statements such as, "Here, there were a lot on 56 and over here, there were a lot on 52," ask students what that tells them about the heights of fourth graders and first graders.

### Professional Development

❷ **Teacher Note:** Focusing on the Shape of the Data, p. 123

- How are the data spread out in the first-grade data, compared with the fourth-grade data? Are the data from one grade more spread out than the data from the other grade?

- How do the clumps of height data compare? Are there similar clumps of similar sizes? Are more than half the data concentrated between certain heights in one class? What about the other?

- Are there outliers in either set of data? How far away are the outliers from the rest of the data?

A few days ago we talked about the typical height in our fourth-grade class. According to your data, what would you say is a fairly typical height in this first-grade class?

Continue to help students establish a clump of values that could be considered typical or usual. Also encourage students to think about how much of the class those data represent. ❷

### Students might say:

 "More than half the first graders are between 48 and 52 inches tall."

Finally, ask students what their response is to the question that started this data investigation: How much taller is a fourth grader than a first grader?

So now we have plenty of information about how the heights of our fourth-grade class and the first-grade class compare. According to this information, about how much taller would you say a fourth grader is than a first grader?

Make sure that students give evidence from the data to support their responses. You might record students' responses on a piece of chart paper so that students can see the variety of responses.

If students do not bring up the small sample size you used to answer the question about how much taller a fourth grader is than a first grader, bring it up yourself.

We collected data only from our class and from one first-grade class. If we collected first-grade height data and fourth-grade height data from many different classes, how do you think this would change your ideas about how much taller a fourth grader is than a first grader?

Students will need their representations and lists of data in Session 1.5.❸ Also, keep students' representations of the height data posted so that students can use them to consider how to represent their data during Session 2.4 of the next Investigation.

### Teaching Note

❸ **Cavity Data** Collect students' cavity data from *Student Activity Book* page 6. Compile all the data in a list. Do not use students' names since some students may feel sensitive about this information. Make one copy of the data for each student for use in the assessment in Session 1.5. If you prefer not to use data from your class, plan to use the set of data provided on Cavity Data from a Fourth-Grade Class (M9).

---

## SESSION FOLLOW-UP

# Daily Practice

 **Daily Practice:** For ongoing review, have students complete *Student Activity Book* page 8.

 **Student Math Handbook:** Students and families may use *Student Math Handbook* pages 94–97 for reference and review. See pages 154–157 in the back of this unit.

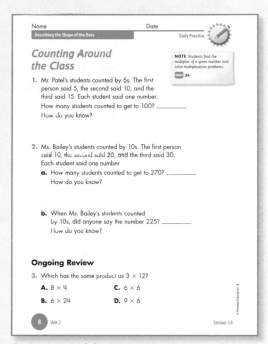

▲ **Student Activity Book, p. 8**

# Assessment: Comparing Numbers of Cavities

## Math Focus Points

◆ Finding the median of a data set

◆ Using medians to compare groups

◆ Considering what information a median does and does not provide

### Vocabulary

**median**

| Today's Plan | | Materials |
|---|---|---|
| **ACTIVITY** **①** **Finding Medians of Height Data** | 15 MIN  CLASS  PAIRS | • Representations of first and fourth graders' heights; Our Class Heights list; Heights of First Graders list |
| **DISCUSSION** **②** **Comparing Medians of Height Data** | 15 MIN  CLASS | |
| **ASSESSMENT ACTIVITY** **③** **Comparing Numbers of Cavities** | ✓  30 MIN  INDIVIDUALS | • M7–M8* • Cavity data for the class or M9* |
| **SESSION FOLLOW-UP** **④** **Daily Practice** | | • *Student Activity Book*, p. 9 • *Student Math Handbook*, pp. 92–93 |

*See *Materials to Prepare*, p. 21.

## Ten-Minute Math

*Quick Survey*  For the survey, ask the class, "What is the color of your eyes?" or a different categorical question that you or the students choose. Make sure that the data they collect is something they already know or can easily observe. With today's data, make a table. Ask the following:

• What do you notice about the data? What does the data tell us about our class?

**ACTIVITY**

# ① Finding Medians of Height Data

**15 MIN   CLASS   PAIRS**

For this activity, display the line plot of the class's height data that was done in the last session.

In the investigation about heights, you shared your ideas about what a typical height might be for a first grader and for a fourth grader. You used a few different ways to decide the height or the range of heights you thought was typical for a fourth grader.

Review some of the ways students decided on typical heights for fourth graders and first graders.

Statisticians are people who work with data. I'm going to show you a method that statisticians sometimes use when they are describing data. They find a landmark number called the **median.❶** Median means *middle.* The *median* is the exact middle of the data when all the data are put in order. Let's find the median of our heights by lining up in order of height and finding the middle.

If students have already come up with this method during previous investigations, point out that they invented this for themselves, just the way a mathematician once invented it.❷

Have the students line up by height. To find the middle, students might sit down in pairs—one from the short end, one from the tall end—until only one or two students are left.

If there is an odd number of students, the median is the value of the height of the middle student when they line up in order of height. If there is an even number of students, the median is the value midway between the heights of the two middle students.❸

After you have established the median height, ask students how they would find the median value on a line plot of their heights. Refer the students to the line plot of their class heights. Ask for ideas about methods they could use to find the median value by using only the numbers.

How can you find the exact middle height, the median, of the class by using the data on this line plot? It was easy to find the middle when we all lined up, but when you see the data like this on a graph, how can you find the middle one? We need a method to use with the numbers on the graph because, in most cases, when statisticians have collected data, they can't "line up" the real things.

**Teaching Note**

❶ **Median, Not Medium** Be sure to write the word *median* on the board and draw attention to its spelling and pronunciation. Many students think that this word is *medium* when they first hear it.

**Professional Development**

❷ **Teacher Note:** Finding and Using the Median, p. 125

**Math Note**

❸ **Finding the Median** Explain that when the median was invented, statisticians decided that when there is an even number of values in a data set, the median would be the value midway between the values of the two middle pieces of data.

## Math Notes

**❹ The Middle of the Data** A common error made by students in finding the median is to find the middle of the values in the data set rather than the middle of all the pieces of data. That is, students count each value only once, rather than counting the value of every piece of data. For example, if there are 6 students with a height of 52 inches, they count this value once rather than 6 times. If this issue comes up in your class, bring it up during the discussion of comparing median heights. Ask, "Why do we count every piece of data to find the middle?"

You know what the median value of your heights is, but I want you to work with your partner to come up with a method for finding the median value by using the line plot. Remember that you need a method that is something like lining up all the values in order to find the middle. After you figure out a method that works with our heights, find the median of the first-grade heights.

Students work in pairs to find the median height by using the set of data. They can use their representations completed in the previous session and their lists of heights.❹

## ONGOING ASSESSMENT: Observing Students at Work

Students find the median of two sets of data.

- **Do students choose a method that makes sense for finding the median?**

- **What method do they use?**

As students work, ask students to explain their methods for finding the median. You may want to have them check by using a different method.

DISCUSSION

## 2 Comparing Medians of Height Data

**15 MIN    CLASS**

### Math Focus Points for Discussion

◆ Using medians to compare groups

◆ Considering what information a median does and does not provide

Ask students to share the values they found for the median heights in each group. If students found different values for the median, choose a way to check together, and decide which value is correct.

Spend a few minutes discussing the fourth-grade median by asking some of the following questions:

- What was the middle height, the median?

- What does that number tell us about the heights in our class?

- If you knew that the median height of some other class was 56 inches, what would you know about that other class?

- What wouldn't you know?

**Students might say:**

"We wouldn't know the range of the data."

"We wouldn't know how spread out or close together the data are."

"We wouldn't know where the clumps of data are or whether there are any really unusual values in the data."

Emphasize that the median does provide important information—that half the students have heights equal to or less than the median and half the students have heights equal to or greater than the median. Guide them toward the conclusion that the median provides one important landmark but does not give a complete picture.

Knowing the median along with the lowest and highest values provides a more complete picture of the data. Write the lowest values, medians, and highest values for both first and fourth grades on the board.

*We have found out the median, or the middle, of the height data from our class and the median of the height data from the first-grade class.*

Ask students how these numbers can help them compare the two groups by asking some of the following questions:

- *How do the groups compare? How many more inches is the median height for our class than the median height of the first graders?*

- *Suppose that was all you knew about the data—how can these numbers help you compare the first-grade and fourth-grade heights?*

Students may find that the median values are similar to the values that they said were typical heights for each class. ❺

**Professional Development**

❺ **Dialogue Box:** What Does the Median Tell You?, p. 147

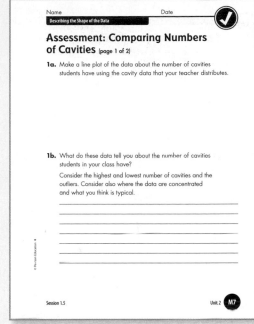

▲ Resource Masters, M7

▲ Resource Masters, M8

**❻ Teacher Note:** Assessment: Comparing Numbers of Cavities, p. 127

Name _____ Date _____

**Describing the Shape of the Data**

### Cavity Data from a Fourth-Grade Class

If you prefer not to use cavity data from your class, you can use the following data instead:

| Name | Number of Cavities |
|------|--------------------|
| Lucy | 0 |
| Andrew | 7 |
| Marisol | 1 |
| Luke | 4 |
| Bill | 0 |
| Jill | 4 |
| Anna | 0 |
| Helena | 0 |
| Kimberly | 12 |
| Derek | 5 |
| Nadeem | 6 |
| Enrique | 0 |
| Noemi | 8 |
| Amelia | 2 |
| Ramona | 3 |
| Cheyenne | 5 |
| Yuki | 7 |
| Ursula | 7 |
| Richard | 5 |
| Venetta | 4 |
| Damian | 5 |
| Abdul | 6 |

Session 1.5    Unit 2 **M9**

▲ Resource Masters, M9

Name _____ Date _____

**Describing the Shape of the Data**    Daily Practice

### Things That Come in Groups

Solve the story problems below. Write a multiplication equation for each problem, and show how you solved it.

**NOTE** Students practice multiplication by solving story problems. [Basic] 40–43

Spiders have 8 legs.

**1.** How many legs are on 5 spiders? _____

Equation: ___ 5 × 8 = ___

**2.** How many legs are on 11 spiders? _____

Equation: _____

**3.** How many legs are on 16 spiders? _____

Equation: _____

**Ongoing Review**

**4.** Which is **not** a factor of 54?

**A.** 3          **C.** 8

**B.** 6          **D.** 9

Session 1.5    Unit 2 **9**

▲ Student Activity Book, p. 9

---

## ③ Comparing Numbers of Cavities

30 MIN  INDIVIDUALS

Distribute the list of cavity data you prepared from *Student Activity Book* page 6 or copies of M9. Students then complete Assessment: Comparing Numbers of Cavities (M7–M8). Students make a line plot of the number of cavities in their class.

Encourage students to connect their descriptions of the data to what it tells them about how the number of cavities in their class compared with the number from the dentist's office.❻

## DIFFERENTIATION: Supporting the Range of Learners

**ELL**   This problem may pose challenges for English Language Learners due to the reading and writing it requires. To help them understand the questions, you can preview the vocabulary *(concentrated, highest amounts, lowest amounts, outliers, typical)* with them before the lesson.  Then highlight these words while you read and re-read the question out loud. While English Language Learners may be able to answer these questions, they may not be able to write their answers. If this is the case, have them tell you the answers while you write what they say. To reinforce the relevant vocabulary and language structures, have students take turns reading the sentences back to you.

**SESSION FOLLOW-UP**

## ④ Daily Practice

**Daily Practice:** For ongoing review, have students complete *Student Activity Book* page 9.

**Student Math Handbook:** Students and families may use *Student Math Handbook* pages 92–93 for reference and review. See pages 154–157 in the back of this unit.

## Mathematical Emphases

**Data Analysis** Representing data

**Math Focus Points**

◆ Representing two sets of data in order to compare them

◆ Using a line plot to represent ordered numerical data

**Data Analysis** Describing, summarizing, and comparing data

**Math Focus Points**

◆ Comparing two sets of data by using the shape and spread of the data

◆ Using medians to compare groups

◆ Considering what information a median does and does not provide

◆ Describing the shape of a set of data: where the data are spread out or concentrated, what the highest and lowest values are, what the range is, and what the outliers are

**Data Analysis** Analyzing and Interpreting data

**Math Focus Points**

◆ Drawing conclusions based on data

◆ Developing arguments based on data

**Data Analysis** Designing and carrying out a data investigation

**Math Focus Points**

◆ Developing and revising a survey question

◆ Recording and keeping track of data

◆ Considering how well a data representation communicates to an audience

# Using Data to Compare

| | Student Activity Book | Student Math Handbook | Professional Development: Read Ahead of Time |
|---|---|---|---|
| **SESSION 2.1**     p. 56 | | | |
| **What Do We Want to Find Out?** Students choose survey questions for comparing two groups. They test their questions, revise them, and make a plan for collecting the data. | 10–13, 15–16 | 87 | • **Teacher Note:** Numerical and Categorical Data, p. 130 <br>• **Dialogue Box:** Refining a Survey Question, p. 149 |
| **SESSION 2.2**     p. 62 | | | |
| **Assessment: Collecting and Comparing Data** Students carry out their surveys with their own class and another class and then begin to represent the data they collected. The work in this session is used as an assessment. | 17–18 | 94, 95, 96 | • **Teacher Note:** Collecting Data from Other Classes, p. 131 |
| **SESSION 2.3**     p. 67 | | | |
| **Representing Survey Data** Students discuss how to create representations to easily compare two sets of data and continue to work on their representations of the survey data. | 19 | 94, 95, 96 | |
| **SESSION 2.4**     p. 71 | | | |
| **What Did You Learn from Your Survey?** Students use their representations of their survey results to develop conclusions about their data. They share what they learned from their surveys with the class. | 20–24 | 97 | |

| Materials to Gather | Materials to Prepare |
|---|---|
| • **Chart paper** | |
| • **M6, Centimeter Grid Paper** (as needed)<br>• **Large pieces of paper** (1 per pair)<br>• **Crayons or markers** (as needed) | • **M10, Assessment Checklist: Collecting and Comparing Data** ☑ Make copies. (several per class)<br>• **Class list** Make copies. (1 per pair)<br>• **Class lists from other classes** Make copies. (1 per pair)<br>• **Representations of first and fourth graders' heights** (from Session 1.3) If they are not still hanging on the walls, post these for reference.<br>• **Data collection schedule** Contact teachers of classes from which your students will collect data and schedule their visits, or have the students schedule their visits. |
| • **M6, Centimeter Grid Paper** (as needed)<br>• **T28, How Do You Get to School? Bar Graph** 🖨<br>• **T29, What Is Your Favorite Mealtime? Bar Graph** 🖨<br>• **Representations of first and fourth graders' heights** (from Session 1.4)<br>• **Large pieces of paper** (1 per pair)<br>• **Crayons or markers** (as needed) | |
| • **Representations of first and fourth graders' heights** (from Session 1.4)<br>• **Representations of survey data** (from Session 2.3) | |

🖨 Overhead Transparency      ☑ Checklist Available

# Using Data to Compare, *continued*

| SESSION 2.5     p. 75 | Student Activity Book | Student Math Handbook | Professional Development: Read Ahead of Time | |
|---|---|---|---|---|
| **Mystery Data**   Students describe and construct theories about three sets of mystery data that each represent the heights or lengths of the members of a group of living things. | 25–29 | 90–91 | • **Teacher Note:** About the Mystery Data, p. 132 | |
| **SESSION 2.6**     p. 81 | | | | |
| **Comparing WNBA Players' Points Per Game** Students examine different possibilities for what data sets with the same median and highest and lowest values could look like. Students compare the number of points per game for two WNBA players. | 26–27, 31–33 | 94–97 | | |
| **SESSION 2.7**     p. 87 | | | | |
| **Is This a Good Game?**   Using the data about the number of points each of two WNBA players scored per game as evidence, students answer questions that require them to make decisions based on the data. | 31–32, 34–38 | 90–91 | • **Dialogue Box:** Is This a Good Game?, p. 151 | |

| Materials to Gather | Materials to Prepare |
|---|---|
| • T30, Mystery Data A 🖶<br>• **Yardstick or tape measure in inches** (1 per class) | |
| • T31, Mystery Data B 🖶<br>• T32–T33, Looking at Mystery Data C (pages 1 and 2 of 2) 🖶 | • **Sample student representations of Mystery Data C (from Session 2.5)** Copy three or four of students' graphs for Mystery Data C, or have the students copy them, onto overhead transparencies or large pieces of paper so they can be easily seen. Choose a plot in which most of the data are concentrated around the median, a plot in which the data are more spread out, and a plot in which the data are grouped into two clumps. |
| | |

🖶 Overhead Transparency

# What Do We Want to Find Out?

## Math Focus Points

◆ Developing and revising a survey question

◆ Recording and keeping track of data

### Vocabulary

**survey**
**numerical data**

| Today's Plan | | | Materials |
|---|---|---|---|
| **ACTIVITY** ① **Brainstorming Survey Questions** | 🕐 20 MIN | 👥 CLASS | • Chart paper |
| **ACTIVITY** ② **Choosing and Revising a Survey Question** | 🕐 30 MIN | 👥 PAIRS | • *Student Activity Book,* pp. 10–12 |
| **DISCUSSION** ③ **What Is Your Question?** | 🕐 10 MIN | 👥 CLASS | |
| **SESSION FOLLOW-UP** ④ **Daily Practice and Homework** | | | • *Student Activity Book,* pp. 13, 15–16 <br> • *Student Math Handbook,* p. 87 |

### Ten-Minute Math

***Today's Number: Broken Calculator*** Students create five expressions that equal 4,250. They must use both addition and subtraction in their expressions. The 4 and 5 keys are broken. Have two or three students give their answers as equations and explain how they know they are correct. (Examples: $6,000 - 2,000 + 228 + 22 = 4,250$ or $1,000 + 3,379 - 129 = 4,250$)

# ACTIVITY

## ① Brainstorming Survey Questions

**20 MIN · CLASS**

For the next few days, students will be working on their own data investigations. Students will develop their own questions and collect data from their own class and at least one other class or group. They will find a way to represent the data, compare the data from the two groups, and come to some conclusions about the data.

There are two requirements for the questions that students develop.

- The questions should result in numerical data: a count or measurement of something (e.g., the number of brothers and sisters you have, the number of hours you sleep or watch TV, the number of places you have lived, the length of time it takes you to get to school, or the distance you live from the school).❶

- The project must involve the comparison of at least two groups (e.g., Who sleeps longer or watches more TV, first graders or fourth graders? Who spends more time getting to school, students who walk or students who ride the bus? How much longer?)

Spend a few minutes explaining this project to students. Let them know that today they begin by developing their survey questions.

Today, you and a partner are going to decide on a survey question that you will use to compare two groups. For example, the two groups could be our class and another class or students and adults.

Over the last week, we have been looking at some numerical data— the number of raisins in a box, and your heights and the first graders' heights. Your survey question also needs to result in numerical data— counts or measurements of something. You will be choosing topics different from those we explored, but thinking about those topics might help you think about some data topics you might be interested in.

Let's brainstorm some survey questions you could ask that would result in some interesting numerical data. Who has an idea for a survey question that you think might be interesting? Remember that the replies people give to your survey question have to be amounts of something.

**Professional Development**

❶ **Teacher Note:** Numerical and Categorical Data, p. 130

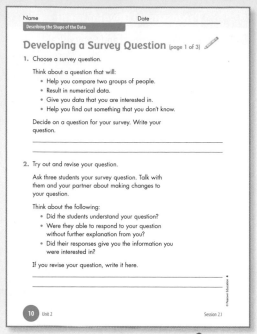

▲ **Student Activity Book, p. 10**

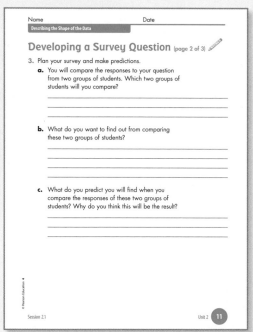

▲ **Student Activity Book, p. 11**

List possible survey questions on a sheet of chart paper. If students bring up survey questions that you know will not result in numerical data (for example, a survey of favorite brands of something or favorite movies), make it clear that, although those survey questions would be interesting to ask, the answers would not be numbers. The answer to such a question would be a brand name or the name of a movie, not a count or measurement.

If students are having difficulty coming up with survey questions, you might add a few suggestions. Here are some possible topics:

• Number of hours people sleep

• Amount of TV watching

• Time it takes to get to school

• Number of teeth lost

• Number of siblings

• Number of pets

• Number of books read in a week

• How long people have lived in their present home

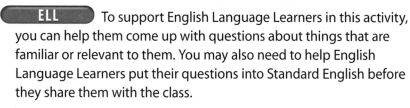

## DIFFERENTIATION: Supporting the Range of Learners

**ELL** To support English Language Learners in this activity, you can help them come up with questions about things that are familiar or relevant to them. You may also need to help English Language Learners put their questions into Standard English before they share them with the class.

## ACTIVITY

**30 MIN  PAIRS**

# Choosing and Revising a Survey Question

Organize the class in pairs that will work together for the duration of the Investigation.❷

Students work in pairs to develop a survey question, following the steps on *Student Activity Book* pages 10–12. Go over the pages with the class, and make sure that students understand what they need to do.

Tell students that they can use one of the survey questions on the list you created together, or they can come up with a different question. Trying out the question with a few other students (see Problem 2) plays a critical part in learning whether their question is understood by others in the way they intend it and whether it will result in the data they want to collect.

Students also need to think through their comparison. They should consider what groups they will survey and what they want to find out in this comparison: Who goes to bed earlier, first graders or fourth graders? Do girls or boys watch more TV? They also make a prediction about what they might learn from their data.

Students also spend some time thinking through how they are going to record and keep track of the data they collect. If you will be able to get class lists from the classes the students will visit, you may suggest a class list as a recording tool.

As students brainstorm, choose, and revise survey questions, help them be mindful that survey questions can bring up sensitive issues for the respondents. Students need to consider how to be respectful of others' feelings in any data collection they do. Someone might feel bad because they cannot have a pet or be embarrassed because they do not read many books in a week. You will want to address such issues as they come up and make sure that you have addressed this issue with students before they begin surveying people outside your classroom. Finding ways to ensure anonymity for respondents may be helpful in some situations.

Name _____ Date _____
Describing the Shape of the Data

**Developing a Survey Question** (page 3 of 3)

4. Plan how to collect and record your data.

Think about the following:
- How are you going to record the data as you collect them?
- What information do you need to write?
- How are you going to keep track of which people you have asked?
- Who is going to do what?

Write how you will record and keep track of your data.

12  Unit 2                                    Session 2.1

▲ **Student Activity Book, p. 12**  WRITING

## Teaching Note

**❸ Revising Survey Questions** Help students keep in mind what they want to find out. Just making a question simpler may not result in relevant and interesting data. For example, "How many sisters and brothers do you have?" may not provide the right information if what students are really interested in is how many children are currently living in the house. In this case, they would want to exclude siblings who no longer live at home and include other children (e.g., a cousin) who do live there.

## Professional Development

**❹ Dialogue Box:** Refining a Survey Question, p. 149

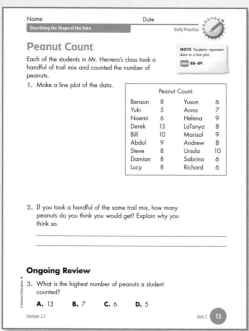

▲ Student Activity Book, p. 13

*Students choose and revise their survey questions.*

## ONGOING ASSESSMENT: Observing Students at Work

Students work on developing a numerical data question for a survey.

- **Will the question give students the information they are interested in?❸**

- **Is the question clear?** How will classmates respond when they try out their question? Are they getting the data they need?

- **Are they considering the details about recording responses and keeping track of whom they have asked?**

As students work on this activity, help them revise their questions. Some students may need to try out a question and revise it several times before they settle on what they think will work.

### DISCUSSION

## 3 What Is Your Question?

🕐 10 MIN   👥 PAIRS

### Math Focus Points for Discussion

◆ Developing and revising a survey question

Ask students to share their initial questions, the revisions they made to their questions, and why they made those changes.❹

## SESSION FOLLOW-UP
# 4 Daily Practice and Homework

 **Daily Practice:** For reinforcement of this unit's content, have students complete *Student Activity Book* page 13.

 **Homework:** Students use two bar graphs to compare data on the number of cubes students in kindergarten and third grade grabbed in one hand. They record their responses on *Student Activity Book* pages 15–16.

 **Student Math Handbook:** Students and families may use *Student Math Handbook* page 87 for reference and review. See pages 154–157 in the back of this unit.

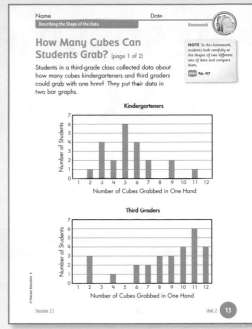

▲ **Student Activity Book, p. 15**

▲ **Student Activity Book, p. 16**

# Assessment: Collecting and Comparing Data

## Math Focus Points

◆ Recording and keeping track of data

◆ Representing two sets of data in order to compare them

| Today's Plan | | Materials |
|---|---|---|
| **ASSESSMENT ACTIVITY**<br>**①** **Assessment: Collecting and Comparing Data** | ✔ 🕐 15 MIN 👥 PAIRS | • M10 ☑<br>• Class list* |
| **ACTIVITY**<br>**②** **Collecting Data from Other Classes** | 🕐 25 MIN 👥 PAIRS | • Class lists from other classes* |
| **ACTIVITY**<br>**③** **Representing Data from Two Groups** | 🕐 20 MIN 👥 PAIRS | • M6<br>• Large pieces of paper; crayons or markers; representations of first and fourth graders' height (from Session 1.4)* |
| **SESSION FOLLOW-UP**<br>**④** **Daily Practice and Homework** | | • *Student Activity Book,* pp. 17–18<br>• *Student Math Handbook,* pp. 94, 95, 96 |

*See *Materials to Prepare,* p. 53.

## Ten-Minute Math

*Today's Number: Broken Calculator*  Students create five expressions that equal 667. They must use both addition and subtraction in their expressions. The 1 and 3 keys are broken. Have two or three students give their answers as equations and explain how they know they are correct. (Examples: $425 + 500 - 258 = 667$ or $824 - 256 + 99 = 667$)

**ASSESSMENT ACTIVITY**

# Collecting and Comparing Data

**15 MIN   PAIRS**

In this session, students collect data from their own class and from another class and begin making representations of the data.❶ If you have made other decisions about when students are going to collect data, you will need to adjust the timing of this session accordingly.

Students will work with partners to collect responses to survey questions from their classmates. Before they begin, they should have a clear system for how they are going to collect and record the responses to their questions. You can suggest recording the responses on a class list.

*Students collect survey data from their classmates.*

Use Assessment Checklist: Collecting and Comparing Data (M10) as you observe students and evaluate their responses on *Student Activity Book* pages 10–12 in this session and as students continue to represent and compare data in Sessions 2.3 and 2.4. This work addresses Benchmark 1: Design an effective survey question to compare two groups and Benchmark 2: Organize and represent data about two groups to compare the groups.

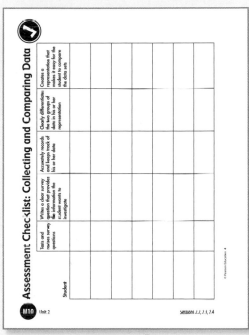

▲ **Resource Masters, M10** ☑

## Professional Development

**Teacher Note:** Collecting Data from Other Classes, p. 131

## ONGOING ASSESSMENT: Observing Students at Work

Students collect and record survey data from their classmates.

- **Are students able to come up with and use an organized system for recording and keeping track of responses?**

- **Do students work together to collect the data?**

This assessment gives you the chance to check on students' understanding of collecting and representing data as you observe their work. The question students design should be tested and revised and should answer what they really want to find out. Students should have clear ideas about collecting and recording their data. As they begin representing data for comparison, the data should be accurately recorded. The data from the two groups should also be easily differentiated and arranged in some way that allows easy comparison of the data sets.

Because students are working in pairs, observing them during these sessions and asking questions to check for understanding helps in assessing individual students. Record information learned from discussions with students and from examining their work on the assessment checklist (M10).

## DIFFERENTIATION: Supporting the Range of Learners

**Intervention** Some students may have a difficult time choosing a good system for recording the data they are collecting. To support these students, you might suggest a system that you think will work for them; for example, using a class list and writing students' responses next to their names, or writing students' responses and names on self-stick notes and checking off their names on a class list. You may need to help them collect the first few responses until they feel comfortable with the system.

25 MIN  PAIRS

### ACTIVITY

# 2 Collecting Data from Other Classes

Students should collect responses to their survey questions from another class or group. They should have a clear system for how they are going to collect and record the responses to their question. If possible, provide them with class lists from the classrooms they will be visiting as one tool for recording and keeping track of responses.

## ONGOING ASSESSMENT: Observing Students at Work

Students collect and record survey data from another class or group.

- **Are students able to come up with and use an organized system for recording and keeping track of responses?**

- **Do students work together to collect the data?**

ACTIVITY

# Representing Data from Two Groups

20 MIN    PAIRS

After students have collected data from your class and another class (or from two groups of people), they should work with their partners to make representations of the data they collected. They continue to work on their representations during the next session.

Remind students that they should find a way to represent both sets of data so they can easily compare them. Some students may put both sets of data into one representation; others may make two representations. They can refer to the representations students created of the first- and fourth-grade height data as examples of possible ways to represent this new data.

Ask each pair of students to draw a rough draft of their representation before doing a final copy. Then talk with them about their graph and what might help others understand their data. At the beginning of the next session, you will have a discussion with the class about representing the data.

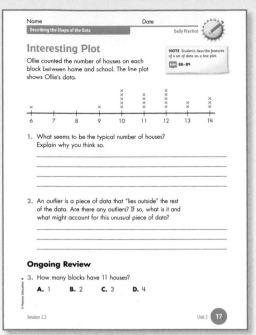

▲ Student Activity Book, p. 17

The page 17 worksheet shows:

Name _____ Date _____

Describing the Shape of the Data — Daily Practice

**Interesting Plot**

Ollie counted the number of houses on each block between home and school. The line plot shows Ollie's data.

NOTE Students describe features of a set of data on a line plot.

1. What seems to be the typical number of houses? Explain why you think so.

2. An *outlier* is a piece of data that "lies outside" the rest of the data. Are there any outliers? If so, what is it and what might account for this unusual piece of data?

**Ongoing Review**

3. How many blocks have 11 houses?

A. 1   B. 2   C. 3   D. 4

Session 2.2 — Unit 2 — 17

The page 18 worksheet shows:

Name _____ Date _____

Describing the Shape of the Data — Homework

**Missing Factors**

Fill in the missing factors in these problems.

NOTE Students practice multiplication combinations ("facts") in related sets.

| 1. | 2. | 3. |
|---|---|---|
| $6 \times \_\_\_\_ = 36$ | $9 \times \_\_\_\_ = 36$ | $\_\_\_\_ \times 12 = 36$ |
| $6 \times \_\_\_\_ = 72$ | $9 \times \_\_\_\_ = 72$ | $\_\_\_\_ \times 12 = 72$ |

| 4. | 5. | 6. |
|---|---|---|
| $\_\_\_\_ \times 8 = 48$ | $11 \times \_\_\_\_ = 44$ | $6 \times \_\_\_\_ = 48$ |
| $\_\_\_\_ \times 8 = 88$ | $11 \times \_\_\_\_ = 88$ | $6 \times \_\_\_\_ = 54$ |

| 7. | 8. | 9. |
|---|---|---|
| $9 \times \_\_\_\_ = 45$ | $\_\_\_\_ \times 7 = 21$ | $\_\_\_\_ \times 8 = 40$ |
| $9 \times \_\_\_\_ = 54$ | $\_\_\_\_ \times 7 = 42$ | $\_\_\_\_ \times 8 = 48$ |
| $9 \times \_\_\_\_ = 63$ | $\_\_\_\_ \times 7 = 84$ | $\_\_\_\_ \times 8 = 56$ |

| 10. | 11. | 12. |
|---|---|---|
| $7 \times \_\_\_\_ = 28$ | $6 \times \_\_\_\_ = 36$ | $\_\_\_\_ \times 12 = 48$ |
| $7 \times \_\_\_\_ = 35$ | $8 \times \_\_\_\_ = 64$ | $\_\_\_\_ \times 12 = 60$ |
| $7 \times \_\_\_\_ = 63$ | $12 \times \_\_\_\_ = 144$ | $\_\_\_\_ \times 12 = 108$ |

18 — Unit 2 — Session 2.2

▲ Student Activity Book, p. 18

*Students begin to make representations of their data.*

## ONGOING ASSESSMENT: Observing Students at Work

Students represent the data they collected from two groups of people.

- **Are students able to use the perspective of an audience as a way to help them present their data?**

- **Do students represent the different groups so that someone looking at the graph can tell which data came from which group?**

- **Do students create representations that allow for an easy comparison of the data sets?**

As students begin to sketch rough drafts of the representations they might use, note any issues or examples you think would be fruitful to bring up in the discussion in the next session.

## SESSION FOLLOW-UP

### 4 Daily Practice and Homework

 **Daily Practice:** For reinforcement of this unit's contents, have students complete *Student Activity Book* page 17.

 **Homework:** Students fill in the missing factor in related sets on *Student Activity Book* page 18.

 **Student Math Handbook:** Students and families may use *Student Math Handbook* pages 94, 95, 96 for reference and review. See pages 154–157 in the back of this unit.

# Representing Survey Data

## Math Focus Points

◆ Considering how well a data representation communicates information to an audience

◆ Representing two sets of data in order to compare them

**Vocabulary**

line plot
bar graph

| Today's Plan | | Materials |
|---|---|---|
| **① DISCUSSION** **How Are You Representing Your Data?** | 🕐 15 MIN  👪 CLASS | • T28; T29 📖 • Representations of first and fourth graders' heights (from Session 1.4) |
| **② ACTIVITY** **Representing Data from Two Groups** | 🕐 45 MIN  👫 PAIRS | • M6 • Large paper; crayons or markers |
| **③ SESSION FOLLOW-UP** **Daily Practice** | | • *Student Activity Book,* p. 19 • *Student Math Handbook,* pp. 94, 95, 96 |

## Ten-Minute Math

*Quick Survey*  For the survey, ask the class, "What is your favorite sport to play?" or a different categorical question that you or the students choose. Make sure that the data they collect is something they already know or can observe easily. With today's data, make a bar graph. Ask the following:

- What do you notice about the data?
- What does the data tell us about our class?

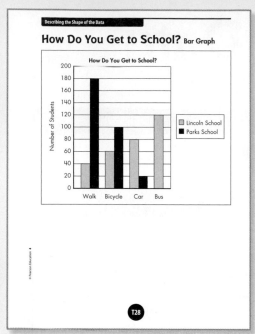

Describing the Shape of the Data

**How Do You Get to School?** Bar Graph

T28

▲ Transparencies, T28 🖳;
Resource Masters, M11

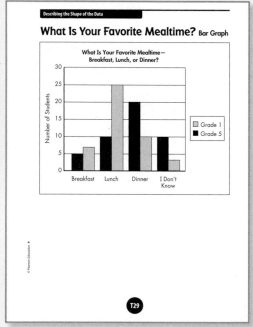

Describing the Shape of the Data

**What Is Your Favorite Mealtime?** Bar Graph

T29

▲ Transparencies, T29 🖳;
Resource Masters, M12

**DISCUSSION**

# How Are You Representing Your Data?

15 MIN    CLASS

## Math Focus Points for Discussion

◆ Representing two sets of data in order to compare them

◆ Considering how well a data representation communicates to an audience

Have a short discussion about the important elements for students to consider as they represent their data.

You have all begun to make representations of your data. First of all, let's think about the different ways you can represent the data you collected. I noticed that [Emaan] and [Steve] are using line plots. How will you help your audience compare your two groups when they look at your line plots? [Noemi] and [Damian], you arc using line plots, too. What are you thinking about as you make your representation?

### Students might say:

"We made the two line plots with exactly the same length, with the same spaces between the numbers. We put one below the other, so that way people can just look back and forth to see how they're the same and different."

"We put our information on the same plot, but we used red for the data from our classroom and green for the data from the other classroom."

There are other kinds of graphs, as well. [Sabrina] and [LaTanya] are using bar graphs. Are there certain things you are thinking about to help make your bar graphs clear to someone who comes in to look at our work?

Some students may remember using bar graphs that show two groups in Grade 3. To remind students about bar graphs, show the transparencies of "How Do You Get to School?" Bar Graph (T28) and "What Is Your Favorite Mealtime?" Bar Graph (T29) as examples of using bar graphs to compare two groups.

Students may have invented their own ways of representing the data. Make sure that several different representations are shared. You can also call students' attention to representations they used for comparing first- and fourth-grade heights that they considered effective in showing the data.

It is important that you and others can look at your representation and easily gather information from it. You are all representing at least two groups—for example, [Enrique] and [Bill] are comparing fourth graders and first graders, as we did for heights. [Jill] and [Anna] are comparing boys and girls, using both our class and the other two fourth grades. You want your audience to be able to easily compare your groups.❶

List students' ideas about what makes an effective representation on the board. Remind students that they should use some of these ideas to revise their representations.

**ACTIVITY**

## 2 Representing Data from Two Groups

**45 MIN   PAIRS**

Students continue to work on their representations of the data. As students return to their work, circulate around the class to look at students' representations. If there are students whose representations are hard to use to compare the data, remind them of some of the suggestions made by other students. Ask questions such as the ones below:

- What was your survey question? I don't see it anywhere on your representation.

- Who were the two groups? How can I tell that from what I see here?

- How can I tell which data is from which group?

- What would help someone who is seeing your representation for the first time compare the third graders with our class?

All students should make the final drafts of their representations easy to understand. Encourage students to make their final representations large and easy to read, but discourage them from spending time on decoration that does not help make their data clear to an audience. Different colors or symbols can be used effectively to help distinguish between groups, but excess decoration can actually take attention away from the data and can be very time consuming.

**Teaching Note**

❶ **Audience** Anticipating a real audience for their work helps students think about how to develop effective representations of their data. If possible, plan a time for parents, the principal, or students from other classes to view the completed representations. Refer to this potential audience during this discussion.

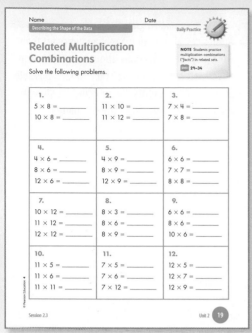

▲ Student Activity Book, p. 19

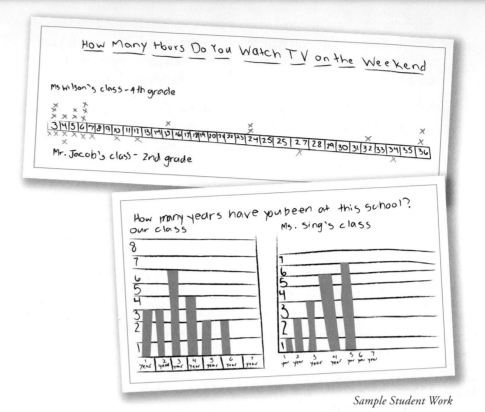

*Sample Student Work*

---

## ONGOING ASSESSMENT: Observing Students at Work

- **Are students able to use the perspective of an audience as a way to help them present their data?**

- **Do students represent the different groups so that someone looking at the graph can tell which data came from which group?**

- **Do students create a representation or representations that allow for an easy comparison of the data sets?**

---

### SESSION FOLLOW-UP

## 3 Daily Practice

**Daily Practice:** For ongoing review, have students complete *Student Activity Book* page 19.

**Student Math Handbook:** Students and families may use *Student Math Handbook* pages 94, 95, 96 for reference and review. See pages 154–157 in the back of this unit.

# What Did You Learn from Your Survey?

## Math Focus Points

◆ Comparing two sets of data by using the shape and spread of the data

◆ Drawing conclusions based on data

### Vocabulary
conclusion

| Today's Plan | | Materials |
|---|---|---|
| **ACTIVITY** ❶ **Analyzing Data** | 30 MIN · PAIRS | • *Student Activity Book,* pp. 20–21 <br> • Representation of first and fourth graders' heights (from Session 1.4) |
| **DISCUSSION** ❷ **Sharing Data Projects** | 30 MIN · CLASS | • Completed representations of survey data (from Session 2.3) |
| **SESSION FOLLOW-UP** ❸ **Daily Practice and Homework** | | • *Student Activity Book,* pp. 22–24 <br> • *Student Math Handbook,* p. 97 |

## Ten-Minute Math

*Today's Number: Broken Calculator*  Students create five expressions that equal 1,130. They must use addition or subtraction in their expressions. The 1 and 3 keys are broken. Have two or three students give their answers as equations and explain how they know they are correct. (Examples: $5,650 - 4,520 = 1,130$ or $890 + 240 = 1,130$)

## Teaching Note

**❶ Writing Project** As a writing project, you may want to have students write a more complete report about their project, which they can post with their representation. They can use what they wrote on *Student Activity Book* pages 20–21 as a rough draft for this report.

Name _____ Date _____

Describing the Shape of the Data

**What Did You Learn From Your Survey?** (page 1 of 2)

1. What was your survey question?

_____
_____

2. Suppose that a teacher was interested in your survey and asked, "What did you learn from your survey?" Write at least three things you learned. Give evidence from the data.

_____
_____
_____
_____
_____
_____

20 Unit 2                              Session 2.4

▲ Student Activity Book, p. 20

### ACTIVITY

## ① Analyzing Data

30 MIN   PAIRS

After students have finished creating their representations from Session 2.3, have them use these representations to draw some conclusions from the data. They will record their ideas on *Student Activity Book* pages 20–21.

Take some time to discuss any questions that are not clear to students before students begin working.

In particular, focus on Problem 2.

For Problem 2, you write about what you learned from your survey. Let's think about the data we collected on the heights of students in our class and in a first-grade class. What did we learn about the heights of these first and fourth graders?

Have two or three students respond.

**Students might say:**

"I learned that fourth graders were about 5 inches taller than first graders."

"The range of heights in the first grade was bigger than the range of heights in the fourth grade."

As students offer these examples, ask them to justify their statements by referring to the data.

When statisticians draw conclusions from data, they justify their conclusions by showing what in the data made them come to that conclusion. What evidence are you using from the height data when you say that the fourth graders were 5 inches taller than the first graders?

Tell students they will write about what they learned from their own survey. Remind them that they should present evidence from their survey and that they need to help their audience understand their project.

Students work with their partners to answer the questions on *Student Activity Book* pages 20–21.❶

## ONGOING ASSESSMENT: Observing Students at Work

Students draw conclusions about their data.

- **Can students use their representations to compare groups?**

- **Can students draw some conclusions from their data?** Can students use evidence from the data to support their conclusions?

- **Can students come up with some more questions related to their survey topic that they could explore?**

As students are writing, remind them to look at the shape of the data for each group. Ask questions such as the following:

- How is the shape of one group similar to and different from the other? Are the ranges similar or different? Are the data concentrated in similar places for the two groups or not? If you found the median, do the two medians divide the data in half at close to the same value, or is one median higher or lower than the other?

*Students analyze the data from their surveys.*

---

Name _____ Date _____

Describing the Shape of the Data

### What Did You Learn From Your Survey? (page 2 of 2)

3. How did the results of your survey compare with your predictions?

_____

_____

_____

4. Now that you have learned some things about your question, can you think of some other survey questions that you would ask to learn more about this topic?

_____

_____

_____

_____

5. What else did you learn about data investigations from doing this project?

_____

_____

_____

Session 2.4                                          Unit 2   **21**

▲ **Student Activity Book, p. 21**

---

Name _____ Date _____

Describing the Shape of the Data                    Daily Practice

### Division With Remainders

**NOTE** Students practice solving division problems and interpreting remainders in story problem contexts.

48–49

1. Fifty people are waiting in line for the roller coaster. Each car holds 8 people. How many cars will the 50 people fill?

   Division equation: _____ ÷ _____ = _____    Answer: _____

2. Forty people bought tickets for a boat ride. Twelve people can ride in a boat at a time. How many boats will the 40 people fill?

   Division equation: _____ ÷ _____ = _____    Answer: _____

3. How many prizes could you get with 50 tickets?

   Division equation:

   _____ ÷ _____ = _____

   Answer: _____

   ARCADE PRIZES
   6 Tickets per prize!

4. The students in Mr. Brown's class counted around the class by 5s. Each student said one number. The number they ended with was 65. How many students counted?

   Division equation: _____ ÷ _____ = _____    Answer: _____

### Ongoing Review

5. The students in Ms. Jones' class counted around the class by 4s. Each student said one number. There are 29 students in her class. Which of these numbers did they say?

   **A.** 120     **B.** 100     **C.** 50     **D.** 10

**22**   Unit 2                                      Session 2.4

▲ **Student Activity Book, p. 22**

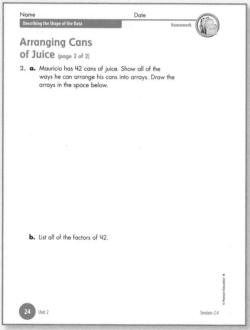

▲ Student Activity Book, p. 23

▲ Student Activity Book, p. 24

## DISCUSSION

# 2 Sharing Data Projects

30 MIN   CLASS

## Math Focus Points for Discussion

◆ Drawing conclusions based on data

Post students' representations around the room. Have students spend about 10 minutes looking at the representations. Assign each pair another pair's representation to look at carefully. Ask them to write down at least one question, one comment, and one thing they learned from the representation. As time permits, pairs can also look at other representations.

After 10 minutes, gather the class together to discuss their observations and comments. Ask everyone to hand their comments and what they learned to the pair who made the representation they looked at. Give the pairs a little time to look at the written comments. Then ask each pair to briefly share one thing they learned and the evidence from the data that supports their conclusion. They can also share, if time permits, one of the comments or questions they received and their response to it.

## SESSION FOLLOW-UP

# 3 Daily Practice and Homework

**Daily Practice:** For ongoing review, have students complete *Student Activity Book* page 22.

**Homework:** Students find factors by arranging numbers into rectangular arrays on *Student Activity Book* pages 23–24.

**Student Math Handbook:** Students and families may use *Student Math Handbook* page 97 for reference and review. See pages 154–157 in the back of this unit.

# Mystery Data

## Math Focus Points

◆ Developing arguments based on data

◆ Using a line plot to represent ordered numerical data

◆ Using medians to compare groups

| Today's Plan | | Materials |
|---|---|---|
| **DISCUSSION** **① Describing Mystery Data A** | 20 MIN · CLASS · PAIRS | • *Student Activity Book,* p. 25<br>• T30<br>• Yardstick or tape measure in inches; chart paper |
| **ACTIVITY** **② Mystery Data B and C** | 40 MIN · PAIRS | • *Student Activity Book,* pp. 25–27<br>• Blank transparencies or chart paper (optional) |
| **SESSION FOLLOW-UP** **③ Daily Practice and Homework** | | • *Student Activity Book,* pp. 28–29<br>• *Student Math Handbook,* pp. 90–91 |

## Ten-Minute Math

***Today's Number: Broken Calculator*** Students create five expressions that equal 589. They must use only addition in their expressions. The 5, 8, and 9 keys are broken. Have two or three students give their answers as equations and explain how they know they are correct. (Examples: $446 + 143 = 589$ or $234 + 332 + 23 = 589$)

## Professional Development

❶ **Teacher Note:** About the Mystery Data, p. 132

## Teaching Note

❷ **Understanding Representations** Mystery Data A and B are both presented in two ways—a table of individual values (ungrouped data), and a line plot showing how often each value occurs (data grouped by value, sometimes called a frequency distribution). As students work with these data, check in to make sure that they understand how to interpret both representations.

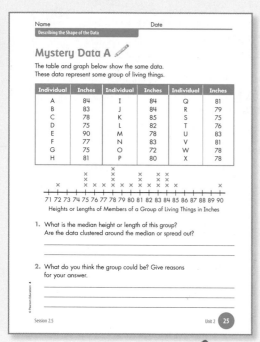

▲ **Student Activity Book, p. 25; Resource Masters, M13; T30**

---

20 MIN · CLASS · PAIRS

### DISCUSSION

# ① Describing Mystery Data A

## Math Focus Points for Discussion

◆ Developing arguments based on data

◆ Using medians to compare groups

In this session, students work with graphs of "mystery data." The graphs show the values of the data—lengths or heights of some set of living things—but students do not know what the group of living things is. Making reasonable conclusions about what each group could be requires students to look carefully at the shape of the data and draw on their own knowledge of measurement.❶

Show the transparency of Mystery Data A (T30) and have students look at their own copies of this table and graph on *Student Activity Book* page 25.

This page shows the measurements of 24 individual members of some group of living things. Your task is to develop a theory about what this group might be by looking carefully at the data.

The table shows the measurement of each living thing. The line plot shows the same data in a different way.❷ Don't tell me any of your theories yet about what these things might be.

Help students use the data from their own classes' heights and other knowledge they have of heights to visualize the heights (or lengths) of the things in Mystery Data A by asking some of the following questions:

• First, what do these numbers tell us about the height or length of these things?

• About how long or tall are these things?

• How do they compare with our own heights?

Use the yardstick or tape measure to help students visualize, for example, how tall 80 inches is in relation to the doorway of the classroom.

Then ask students to describe the shape of the data in the same way they have for other sets of data. Make sure that students describe the data in terms of what information they convey about the group of living things.

**Students might say:**

"The shortest one is 72 inches, and the tallest one is 90 inches."

"There are many of them in the high 70s and low 80s."

Finally, ask students to find the median height in this group. Students can work on this in pairs briefly. Then prompt them to share their ideas by asking them some of the following questions:

- What is the median value for this set of data? How did you find it?

- Are most of the data clustered around the median, or are the data very spread out?

- How does the median of this data set compare with the median of our class heights?

- Would you say that the median gives a pretty good indication of what to expect for the heights (or lengths) of these living things?

Ask students to consider what the Mystery Data are.

*Now that we have a good sense of how tall or long these mystery beings are, let's brainstorm what they could be. I'm interested in your theories, but I'm also interested in your reasons for your theories and whether you agree or disagree with theories other people come up with.*

Record students' theories on chart paper, and keep it posted. Keep the identity of this first set of data a mystery for now.

## ACTIVITY

### ②Mystery Data B and C

🕐 40 MIN  👥 PAIRS

Students work in pairs on *Student Activity Book* pages 25–27. They have already discussed Mystery Data A, but now they can fill in their own answers. Then students find the median for Mystery Data B, describe the shape of the data set, and write what they think this group might be. For Mystery Data C, they create a line plot and consider what these data represent.

Ask students to look at *Student Activity Book* page 27. Explain that on this page they are given the median, the highest and lowest values for the data,

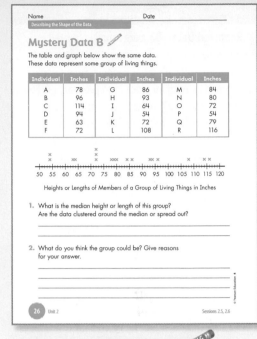

▲ **Student Activity Book, p. 26;**
**Resource Masters, M14; T31**

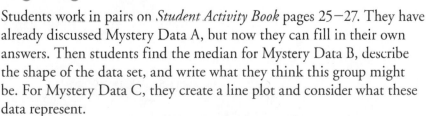

▲ **Student Activity Book, p. 27**

### Teaching Note

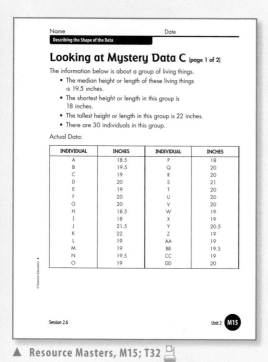

❸ **Reported Data** Data are usually reported in the form of one or a few important values that represent the data set as a whole. For example, the median gasoline price from February 26, 2005, through March 27, 2005, in Massachusetts was $1.97 per gallon, and values ranged from $1.85 to $2.07. We receive data in this form every day. From these few numbers, we form a picture of what the data are like without having to see the entire set. When students develop a line plot for Mystery Data C, they have this experience of picturing a data set on the basis of a few given values.

Name _____ Date _____

Describing the Shape of the Data

#### Looking at Mystery Data C (page 1 of 2)

The information below is about a group of living things.
- The median height or length of these living things is 19.5 inches.
- The shortest height or length in this group is 18 inches.
- The tallest height or length in this group is 22 inches.
- There are 30 individuals in this group.

Actual Data:

| INDIVIDUAL | INCHES | INDIVIDUAL | INCHES |
|---|---|---|---|
| A | 18.5 | P | 18 |
| B | 19.5 | Q | 20 |
| C | 19 | R | 20 |
| D | 20 | S | 21 |
| E | 19 | T | 20 |
| F | 20 | U | 20 |
| G | 20 | V | 20 |
| H | 18.5 | W | 19 |
| I | 18 | X | 19 |
| J | 21.5 | Y | 20.5 |
| K | 22 | Z | 19 |
| L | 19 | AA | 19 |
| M | 19 | BB | 19.5 |
| N | 19.5 | CC | 19 |
| O | 19 | DD | 20 |

Session 2.6    Unit 2 **M15**

▲ **Resource Masters, M15; T32**

---

and the number of pieces of data. From this information, they need to make a line plot of what they think the data might look like and come up with a theory about what group of living things the data might represent.❸ Emphasize that in making a line plot of Mystery Data C, they are making only a theoretical line plot. There is no way they can know for sure how the data are spread out in this data set, but they should think about what might be reasonable. You may also want to remind students that lengths and heights do not have to be in whole inches.

### ONGOING ASSESSMENT: Observing Students at Work

Students describe two sets of mystery data and develop theories about the subject of the data.

- **Can students find the median for Mystery Data B?**

- **Are students able to create a line plot from the median, highest and lowest values, and number of pieces of data for Mystery Data C?**

- **Are students supporting their theories with plausible reasons, using what they already know about the height of living objects and the characteristics of the data set?**

In preparation for the discussion of this work in the next session, choose several of the students' plots that show different possibilities for the values of Mystery Data C. For example, choose a plot in which most of the data are concentrated around the median, a plot in which the data are more spread out, and a plot in which the data are grouped into two clumps. Copy these graphs, or have students copy them, onto overhead transparencies or large sheets of paper so that the class can easily see them.

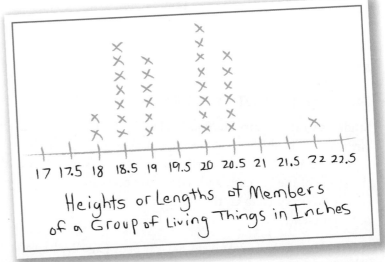

*Sample Student Work*

# DIFFERENTIATION: Supporting the Range of Learners

**Intervention** For students who can mark the median and the highest and lowest values on the line plot but seem baffled about how to figure out the rest of the data points, it may be helpful for them to first make a list of what the data could be. Help them write 18 (the lowest value) and 22 (the highest value) with 28 blank lines between these values. Talk through where the median value is, and note this on their list. Because there are 30 pieces of data, the median value of 19.5 must fall midway between the middle two values.

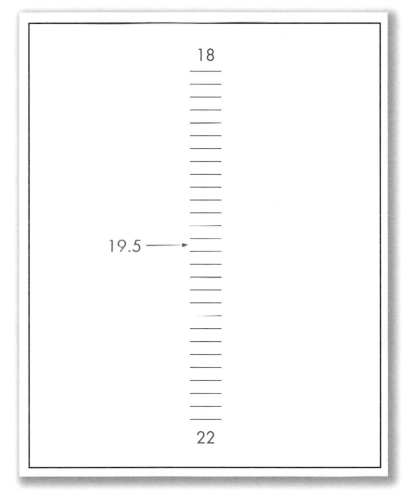

Now they can fill in what the other values could be. After they fill in these values in their list, they can transfer them, one at a time, to a line plot. This strategy is also helpful for students who quickly mark points on the line plot without thinking through what those points can be, given the information they have.

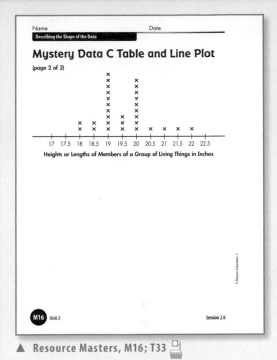

▲ Resource Masters, M16; T33

## Student Activity Book, p. 28

Name _____ Date _____

Describing the Shape of the Data

Daily Practice

### Parking Lot Data

The students in Ms. May's class counted the cars in the school parking lot at the beginning of every school day for a month.

**NOTE** Students represent and describe a set of data.

SMH 88–91

1. Represent the data in a table, a line plot, or with tallies.

| Number of Cars in the Parking Lot | | | | |
|---|---|---|---|---|
| 18 | 23 | 22 | 25 | 20 |
| 23 | 19 | 17 | 24 | 23 |
| 22 | 23 | 25 | 24 | 24 |
| 22 | 23 | 22 | 24 | 25 |

2. Describe the data. Try to include a discussion of the range, how it clumps or spreads out, whether there are any outliers, and what is typical.

_____
_____
_____
_____

### Ongoing Review

3. What is the median number of cars in the parking lot?

A. 20    B. 21    C. 22    D. 23

28    Unit 2                                    Session 2.5

## Student Activity Book, p. 29

Name _____ Date _____

Describing the Shape of the Data

Homework

### Things That Come in Groups

Solve the story problems below. Write a multiplication equation for each problem, and show how you solved it.

**NOTE** Students solve multiplication problems and write an equation to represent each problem.

SMH 40–43

Insects have 6 legs.

1. How many legs do 9 insects have? _____

   Equation: _____

2. How many legs do 11 insects have? _____

   Equation: _____

3. How many legs do 20 insects have? _____

   Equation: _____

Session 2.5                                    Unit 2    29

---

fits the given characteristics, to create a second line plot with the same characteristics or to create another plot that has no actual piece of data with a value of 19.5. Because the median is 19.5, many students simply use 19.5 as the value for the two middle pieces of data, but they could be, for example, 19 and 20, 18.5 and 20.5, or 18 and 21.

### SESSION FOLLOW-UP

# 3 Daily Practice and Homework

**Daily Practice:** For reinforcement of this unit's content, have students complete *Student Activity Book* page 28.

**Homework:** Students solve multiplication story problems and write an equation for each problem on *Student Activity Book* page 29.

**Student Math Handbook:** Students and families may use Student Math Handbook pages 90–91 for reference and review. See pages 154–157 in the back of this unit.

# Comparing WNBA Players' Points Per Game

## Math Focus Points

◆ Developing arguments based on data

◆ Considering what information a median does and does not provide

◆ Describing the shape of a set of data: where the data are spread out or concentrated, what the highest and lowest values are, what the range is, and what the outliers are

◆ Comparing two sets of data by using the shape and spread of the data

### Vocabulary

**value**

| Today's Plan | | Materials |
|---|---|---|
| **DISCUSSION** **❶ Mystery Data** | 20 MIN   CLASS | • *Student Activity Book*, pp. 26–27 (from Session 2.5) • T31–T33 • Sample student representations of Mystery Data C (from Session 2.5)* |
| **ACTIVITY** **❷ Comparing WNBA Players' Points Per Game** | 40 MIN   PAIRS | • *Student Activity Book*, pp. 31–32 |
| **SESSION FOLLOW-UP** **❸ Daily Practice** | | • *Student Activity Book*, p. 33 • *Student Math Handbook*, pp. 94–97 |

*See *Materials to Prepare*, p. 55.

## Ten-Minute Math

***Today's Number: Broken Calculator***  Students create five expressions that equal 1,412. They must use only subtraction in their expressions. The 0, 1, and 2 keys are broken. Have two or three students give their answers as equations and explain how they know they are correct. (Examples: $6{,}798 - 5{,}386 = 1{,}412$ or $5{,}347 - 3{,}935 = 1{,}412$)

## Math Note

**① Describing the Data** Students may notice that there is a large range; 62 inches (over 5 feet) separate the lowest and highest values. There are no large clumps of data. About $\frac{2}{3}$ of the data are in the 72- to 96-inch range with a median of 79.5 inches. The data vary from about $4\frac{1}{2}$ ft to almost 10 ft. Clearly these are not human beings.

### DISCUSSION
# ① Mystery Data

20 MIN    CLASS

## Math Focus Points for Discussion

◆ Developing arguments based on the data

◆ Considering what information a median does and does not provide

◆ Describing the shape of a set of data: where the data are spread out or concentrated, what the highest and lowest values are, what the range is, and what the outliers are

Refer students to the Mystery Data B on *Student Activity Book* page 26, or use Transparency (T31). Ask students to describe the data.①

Ask a few students to share their theories about the data and their reasoning behind their theories.

Emphasize that there was no way they could know for sure what these Mystery Data represent. The task was to develop theories that matched the data. If one of the theories is correct, you can reveal what Mystery Data B is—the lengths of 18 boa constrictors living in various museums or zoos in the United States. Otherwise, you will return to figuring out the identity of this group at the end of the discussion.

Show the top part of page 1 of the transparency of Looking at Mystery Data C (T32) with the table of actual data covered. Ask students to share some of the line plots they created of these Mystery Data and encourage students to look at the different ways students thought the shape of the data might look.

Ask some of the following questions.

• What do you notice about how they are similar and how they are different?

• How are the data spread out in the different line plots you made?

• Do they all have a median of 19.5?

• Are there any you want us to check together to make sure?

Uncover the bottom part of the transparency to reveal the table of the actual data for Mystery Data C. Ask students whether they think the line plot for these actual data will be similar to or different from the ones they created.

Then show the line plot on page 2 of the transparency of Mystery Data C Table and Line Plot (T33). Ask students to compare this line plot with the samples you have chosen to show them.

How is it possible that such different data could have the same median, highest, and lowest values? The median and the extreme (highest and lowest) values provide landmarks for the data set. In particular, where the median is in relation to the highest and lowest values provides one indication of how the data are spread out. Landmarks help us imagine what the data look like, but they don't provide all the information that a line plot does about how the data are spread out in each half of the data.❷

Now ask students to share their theories about what Mystery Data C might be and their reasoning behind their theories.

To end this discussion, return to each Mystery Data set, one at a time. Provide some clues to help students eliminate some of the theories they have developed and feel more sure about others. Here are some examples of clues to use.

- Mystery Data A: They were all in Los Angeles at the same time on February 15, 2004.

- Mystery Data B: They are not human. They live in zoos and museums in the United States.

- Mystery Data C: These data were collected in March, 2005. If we measured these same living things now, the data would be different.❸

### ACTIVITY
## 2 Comparing WNBA Players' Points Per Game

**40 MIN    PAIRS**

Introduce the new context for comparing data—points scored by two players in the Women's National Basketball Association (WNBA). The amount of explanation you give about the scoring of basketball depends on the knowledge of your class. You might have some students who are knowledgeable about basketball explain how the game is scored, or you can explain the scoring yourself. This way everyone will become familiar with basketball.

Today you are going to be representing, comparing, and analyzing data about some players in the Women's National Basketball Association (WNBA). You are going to be looking at the number of points two players scored during the games of the 2003 season and comparing them.

**Math Note**

❷ **Landmarks in Data**  By creating and graphing different data sets with the same landmarks, students gain experience in visualizing what information the median and extremes do and do not provide.

**Teaching Note**

❸ **Revealing the Mysteries**  You can play a game of Twenty Questions to reveal the mysteries for each data set, or you can give more clues until the students uncover the mystery. You may want to reveal the solution dramatically; for example, by placing the answer in an envelope that a student can open and read to the class after students have shared their hypotheses.

The number of points scored during a basketball game is important because the team that scores the most points at the end of the game wins. Players score 2 or 3 points for each basket they make, depending on how far away they are from the basket. They score one point for each "free throw," or penalty shot.

Ask students to look at *Student Activity Book* pages 31–32 for this activity.

You are going to be comparing the points Yolanda Griffith and Mwadi Mabika scored during each game they played in the 2003 season. You are given a line plot of the points Mabika scored during each game she played in 2003.

Look together at the line plot and ask students to explain what the Xs stand for on this particular line plot. Point to one X, and ask what information that X tells you. For example, one of the Xs at 12 means that Mabika scored 12 points in one of her games. The column of three Xs at 12 means that there were three different games in which Mabika scored 12 points.

Now help students think through how they will keep track of the data for Yolanda Griffith as they make a line plot of her points per game.

Yolanda Griffith played in 39 games—that is quite a few pieces of data. What can you do to make sure that you get all of those pieces of data on your line plot?

Tell students to share strategies for checking to make sure that they put all of the data on their line plot.

Students spend the remainder of the session completing *Student Activity Book* pp. 31–32. They work in pairs to make the line plot and discuss the answer to the questions, but each student should complete his or her own activity page.❹

Students make line plots to compare two sets of data.

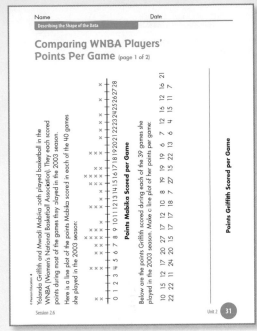

▲ Student Activity Book, p. 31

## ONGOING ASSESSMENT: Observing Students at Work

Students make a line plot of a set of data and compare the data set with another set of data.

- **Can students make an accurate line plot?**

- **Can students use the two line plots to compare the shapes of the data sets?**

- **Do students compare aspects of the shape of the data, such as the highest and lowest values, the outliers, where the data are concentrated, the median, and what is typical of each of the player's points per game?**

As students work, check with them about how they found the median of the data, and ask them to check their work. It is easy to make a mistake with 39 pieces of data.

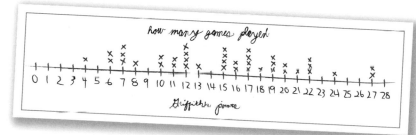

Sample Student Work

▲ Student Activity Book, p. 31

▲ Student Activity Book, p. 32

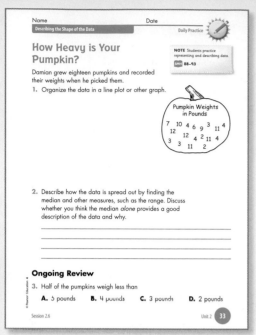

Name _____ Date _____

Describing the Shape of the Data _____ Daily Practice

### How Heavy is Your Pumpkin?

NOTE Students practice representing and describing data.
SMH 88–93

Damian grew eighteen pumpkins and recorded their weights when he picked them.

1. Organize the data in a line plot or other graph.

Pumpkin Weights
in Pounds

7  10  4  6  9  3  11  4
12     12     4  2  11  4
3     3  11  2

2. Describe how the data is spread out by finding the median and other measures, such as the range. Discuss whether you think the median *alone* provides a good description of the data and why.

_____
_____
_____

### Ongoing Review

3. Half of the pumpkins weigh less than

**A.** 5 pounds  **B.** 4 pounds  **C.** 3 pounds  **D.** 2 pounds

Session 2.6  Unit 2  **33**

▲ Student Activity Book, p. 33

## DIFFERENTIATION: Supporting the Range of Learners

**Intervention** For students who need assistance creating an accurate line plot, list or talk through the steps in this process.

- **Determine the range of the data.**

- **Make a line plot that is long enough to include the entire range.**

- **Label the lowest and highest values on the line plot and then mark off all the values in between.**

- **Check or circle each piece of data as you put it on the line plot.**

- **Go back and double-check to make sure that you have all the pieces of data.**

For students who are unsure how to compare the two sets of data, ask them to first describe each data set separately. Suggest that they look at areas with clumps of data and with few data.

*If you went to a game in which Mabika was playing, how many points might you expect her to make? Why?*

After students have described each data set separately, they can use those statements to compare the two players.

### SESSION FOLLOW-UP

## 3 Daily Practice

**Daily Practice:** For reinforcement of this unit's content, have students complete *Student Activity Book* page 33.

**Student Math Handbook:** Students and families may use Student Math Handbook pages 94–97 for reference and review. See pages 154–157 in the back of this unit.

# Is This a Good Game?

## Math Focus Points

◆ Developing arguments based on data

◆ Considering what information a median does and does not provide

| Today's Plan | | Materials |
|---|---|---|
| **ACTIVITY** ❶ **Is This a Good Game?** | 40 MIN · PAIRS · INDIVIDUALS | • *Student Activity Book*, pp. 31–32 (from Session 2.6), 34–35 |
| **DISCUSSION** ❷ **Arguments About WNBA Players** | 20 MIN · CLASS | • *Student Activity Book*, pp. 34–35 |
| **SESSION FOLLOW-UP** ❸ **Daily Practice and Homework** | | • *Student Activity Book*, pp. 36–38 <br> • *Student Math Handbook*, pp. 90–91 |

## Ten-Minute Math

*Quick Survey* For the survey, ask the class, "In how many languages can you say 'hello'?" or a different numerical question that you or the students choose. Make sure that the data they collect is something that they already know or can observe easily. With today's data, make a line plot. Ask the following:

• What do you notice about the data?

• What does the data tell us about our class?

## Teaching Notes

**❶ Making an Argument** You may want to tell students that *making an argument* is what mathematicians call developing reasoning based on evidence. An argument in this sense doesn't mean a disagreement or fight—the meaning most students probably know. Rather, an argument is a line of reasoning based on mathematical or statistical evidence.

**❷ Choose One Question** Keep in mind that you will choose one question for discussion at the end of this session. Look for which questions are most engaging to students and for which questions there is a variety of interesting reasoning.

Name _____ Date _____

*Describing the Shape of the Data*

**Is This a Good Game?** (page 1 of 2)

Use Mabika's and Griffith's points per game to answer the following questions.

1. Barney, who is a big fan of Mwadi Mabika, went to her game on May 28. Mabika scored 10 points. Barney wants to know whether this was a good game or a bad game for Mabika. What is your opinion? Use the data to support your opinion.

2. Venetta, who is a big fan of Yolanda Griffith, went to her game on July 5. Griffith scored 17 points. Venetta wants to know whether this was a good game or a bad game for Griffith. What is your opinion? Use the data to support your opinion.

3. Suppose that you were an owner of a team who was thinking about hiring Mwadi Mabika or Yolanda Griffith. As you decide whom to hire, one of the things you want to look at carefully is the player's points per game. According to their point scoring data, which player do you think you might hire for your basketball team? Why?

 34  Unit 2                     Session 2.7

▲ Student Activity Book, p. 34

---

40 MIN   PAIRS   INDIVIDUALS

# ① Is This a Good Game?

If needed, give students time to finish *Student Activity Book* pages 31–32. Then introduce *Student Activity Book* pages 34–35.

After you have finished your line plot and your comparison, you are going to answer some questions about Mwadi Mabika's and Yolanda Griffith's points per game. When people look at data, they are often using the data to make decisions. That's what you're going to be doing on this sheet. You are going to give your opinions, but you have to use the data to support your opinions—to give good reasons for your decisions.❶

As students work on answering these questions, check in with them to make sure that they are explaining how the data support their ideas.❷ Refer them back to their line plots and their description and comparison of the data on *Student Activity Book* page 31–32.

## ONGOING ASSESSMENT: Observing Students at Work

Students interpret data and explain how the data support their opinions and decisions.

- **Are students looking carefully at the data in order to make a decision?** Are they looking at the data set as a whole instead of looking at individual values? Are they coming to conclusions on the basis of the data?

- **Are students able to gather information from the line plots in order to draw conclusions about the data?**

- **Do students support their ideas with evidence from the data?**

## DIFFERENTIATION: Supporting the Range of Learners

**Intervention** If some students seem stuck or are writing their opinions without reference to the data, ask them to look with you at the line plots. Ask students to point to the part of the line plot they would use to back up their ideas. You might ask students to describe the data first by asking some of the following questions:

- Let's look at Mabika's scores together. Which of these games would be really good games for her, better than she usually plays? Where do you see that on the line plot?

- Which games are really bad games for her, ones she would be disappointed about? Point to that part of the line plot.

- Which of these games are pretty ordinary games for her, ones that she might expect?

- Now, what do you think about 10 points—is that good or bad?

## DISCUSSION

# 2 Arguments About WNBA Players

**20 MIN    CLASS**

## Math Focus Points for Discussion

◆ Developing arguments based on data

Choose one of the problems on *Student Activity Book* pages 34–35 to discuss as a class. Problems 1 and 2, about whether a particular game is a good game for Mabika or Griffith, are a good focus for a discussion in which many students will have something to say. ❸

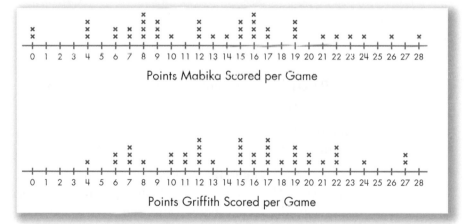

Points Mabika Scored per Game

Points Griffith Scored per Game

Ask students to share their responses and to support their arguments with evidence from the data. Urge students to agree or disagree with other students' arguments, using evidence from the data, but stress that there is not one correct answer to these questions.

Name _____ Date _____

Describing the Shape of the Data

**Is This a Good Game?** (page 2 of 2)

4. Suppose that a sports reporter is writing a story comparing the points Yolanda Griffith and Mwadi Mabika scored during the 2003 season. The reporter is planning to report their median scores. What can the reporter's readers learn from a comparison of their median scores?

_____

_____

_____

_____

5. Do you think this is enough information for readers to know about Griffith's and Mabika's scoring records? If not, what other information do you think the reporter should include?

_____

_____

_____

_____

_____

_____

Session 2.7                Unit 2  **35**

▲ **Student Activity Book, p. 35**

Name _____ Date _____

Describing the Shape of the Data                Daily Practice

**Multiplication Pairs**

NOTE Students practice solving multiplication problems.
SMH 16–17

1. Solve each pair of multiplication problems below.

Use the first problem to help you solve the second problem.

| | |
|---|---|
| $12 \times 8 =$ _____ | $15 \times 6 =$ _____ |
| $24 \times 8 =$ _____ | $30 \times 3 =$ _____ |
| $15 \times 4 =$ _____ | $9 \times 9 =$ _____ |
| $15 \times 8 =$ _____ | $18 \times 9 =$ _____ |
| $32 \times 5 =$ _____ | $8 \times 6 =$ _____ |
| $16 \times 10 =$ _____ | $16 \times 6 =$ _____ |

**Ongoing Review**

2. Which of the following does not equal $12 \times 8$?

   **A.** $24 \times 4$          **C.** $3 \times 28$

   **B.** $2 \times 48$          **D.** $6 \times 16$

**36** Unit 2                Session 2.7

▲ **Student Activity Book, p. 36**

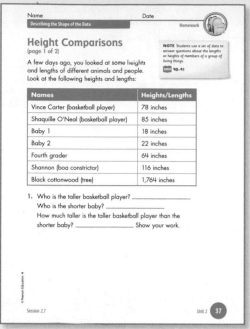

▲ **Student Activity Book, p. 37**

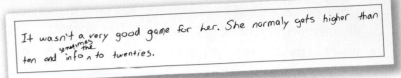

*Sample Student Work*

If you have time, ask students for their answers to Problem 3, or choose a question that seems to generate a variety of arguments.

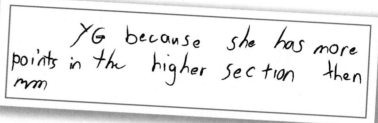

*Sample Student Work*

▲ **Student Activity Book, p. 38**

**SESSION FOLLOW-UP**

## 3 Daily Practice and Homework

**Daily Practice:** For ongoing review, have students complete *Student Activity Book* page 36.

**Homework:** Students use height and length data to solve problems on *Student Activity Book* pages 37–38.

**Student Math Handbook:** Students and families may use *Student Math Handbook* pages 90–91 for reference and review. See pages 154–157 in the back of this unit.

## Mathematical Emphases

**Probability** Describing the probability of an event

**Math Focus Points**

◆ Associating the word *probability* with how likely something is to occur

◆ Arranging events along a line representing the range of *certain* to *impossible*

◆ Using numbers from 0 to 1 as measures of probability

◆ Associating verbal descriptions of probability with numeric descriptions

◆ Comparing the expected probability of an event with the actual results of repeated trials of that event

**Data Analysis** Describing, summarizing, and comparing data

**Math Focus Points**

◆ Comparing two sets of data by using the shape and spread of the data

# Finding and Comparing Probabilities

| | Student Activity Book | Student Math Handbook | Professional Development: Read Ahead of Time | |
|---|---|---|---|---|
| **SESSION 3.1** p. 94 | | | | |
| **Creating a Likelihood Line** Students develop categories that represent a range of probabilities from certain to impossible and think of events that fall in each category. | 39, 41–42 | 98 | | |
| **SESSION 3.2** p. 101 | | | | |
| **Numerical Measures of Probability** Students relate numbers from 0 to 1 to the categories on the Likelihood Line. They use fractions to describe the probabilities of some events. | 41–46 | 99 | • **Teacher Note:** Impossible, Certain, and Everything in Between, p. 134 <br>• **Dialogue Box:** Discussing Probability Experiments, p. 152 | |
| **SESSION 3.3** p. 107 | | | | |
| **Probability Experiments** Students carry out probability experiments, using combinations of two colors of cubes in a container. | 43–44, 47–48 | 99–100 | | |
| **SESSION 3.4** p. 113 | | | | |
| **Comparing Probability Experiments** Students complete three probability experiments and describe and compare the results. | 49–51 | 99–100 | | |
| **SESSION 3.5** p. 117 | | | | |
| **End-of-Unit Assessment** Students work on two End-of-Unit Assessment problems. In the first problem, students place five events on a Likelihood Line. In the second problem, students organize and describe data and compare two data sets. | 52 | 94–98 | • **Teacher Note:** End-of-Unit Assessment, p. 136 | |

| Materials to Gather | Materials to Prepare |
|---|---|
| • **11″ x 17″ or 12″ x 18″ paper** (1 per group of 3)<br>• **Self-stick notes, index cards, or other small paper** (about 10 per group of 3)<br>• **Envelope** (1 per group of 3; optional) | • **Chart paper**  Tape together two sheets of chart paper, the long sides going horizontally (or use butcher paper about 5 feet long). Write the title "Likelihood Line" at the top. Draw a horizontal line 3 to 5 inches from the top across the two pages. Post the Likelihood Line in the classroom. |
| • **Likelihood Line** (from Session 3.1)<br>• **Paper bag or other opaque container**<br>• **Cubes** (2 red; 6 blue)<br>• **Number cube, numbered 1–6** (1 per pair) | |
| • **Chart paper**<br>• **Jar or other clear container**<br>• **Paper bag or other opaque container** (1 per pair)<br>• **Red and blue cubes** (15 of each color per pair, plus 10 more of each color) | • **M17, Record of Cubes in a Bag**  Make copies. (2 per pair, plus extras as needed)<br>• **Chart paper**  Make a blank 0–50 line plot by taping together two sheets of chart paper, the long sides going horizontally (or use butcher paper about 5 feet long). Draw a horizontal line 3 to 5 inches from the bottom across the two sheets. Mark off 50 evenly spaced small lines on the line, and number every fifth one starting with 0. Under the numbers write the title "Number of Red Cubes in 50 Trials." Post the line plot in the classroom.<br>• **Clear container with cubes**  Put 10 red cubes and 10 blue cubes into a jar or other transparent container. |
| • **Materials for probability experiments** (from Session 3.3)<br>• **0–50 line plot** (from Session 3.3)<br>• **List of predictions** (from Session 3.3) | • **M17, Record of Cubes in a Bag**  Make copies as needed. |
| | • **M6, Centimeter Grid Paper**  Make copies. (1 per student; optional)<br>• **M18–M21, End-of-Unit Assessment**  Make copies. (1 per student) |

# Creating a Likelihood Line

## Math Focus Points

◆ Associating the word *probability* with how likely something is to occur

◆ Arranging events along a line representing the range of *certain* to *impossible*

**Vocabulary**

**probability**

| Today's Plan | | Materials |
|---|---|---|
| **ACTIVITY** ① **Introducing Probability and the Likelihood Line** | 20 MIN  CLASS | • Likelihood Line* |
| **ACTIVITY** ② **Creating Events for the Likelihood Line** | 30 MIN  GROUP | • 11" x 17" or 12" x 18" paper; self-stick notes; envelope (optional) |
| **DISCUSSION** ③ **Characterizing Events from Impossible to Certain** | 10 MIN  CLASS | |
| **SESSION FOLLOW-UP** ④ **Daily Practice and Homework** | | • *Student Activity Book,* pp. 39, 41–42 • *Student Math Handbook,* p. 98 |

*See *Materials to Prepare,* p. 93.

## Ten-Minute Math

***Today's Number: Broken Calculator*** Students create five expressions that equal 2,998. They must use only subtraction in their expressions. The 1 and 2 keys are broken. Have two or three students give their answers as equations and explain how they know they are correct. (Examples: 6,003 − 3,005 = 2,998 or 4,570 − 937 − 635 = 2,998)

## ACTIVITY

# ① Introducing Probability and the Likelihood Line

**20 MIN    CLASS**

Briefly introduce the topic of probability. ❶

When people who collect data try to understand what their data tells them, they also use something called probability. For example, suppose that someone in our state wanted to find out whom people are likely to vote for in the next election. [If there is a specific election students are familiar with, you can refer to that.]

They don't have the time or money to ask every voter, so they take a poll—they ask some voters and use that sample to try to predict what all the voters will do. Let's say that they ask 500 voters: 300 say that they'll vote for Candidate A, and 200 say that they'll vote for Candidate B. This result doesn't tell them for sure that Candidate A will win because there are really thousands of voters. However, sometimes a sample such as this does give a pretty good indication of what is going to happen.

There is a special part of mathematics that helps people decide how likely or unlikely it is that the results of their data investigation are actually true for a larger population. We're going to start studying this special part of mathematics, called probability. It has to do with using mathematics to predict future events or to describe situations in which we can't actually see, count, or measure all the cases of something.

Show students the Likelihood Line you prepared. Write *impossible* to the far left above the line.

So let's start out by thinking about what we know about which future events are likely, possible, or impossible. I've drawn a line that we'll call the Likelihood Line. At one end, I've written *Impossible*. Can you think of any future events that are impossible—events you are sure will never, ever happen?

Take a number of suggestions and write them beneath the word *impossible*.

Probability is often used for predicting future outcomes. If students respond by describing a current state of affairs rather than predicting the probability of a future event ("It's impossible that I have a pet cat"), make a distinction between what has already happened and what may happen in the future. Explain that, at this point, you are interested in the probability of future events. For example, "It's impossible that the students in this class will be 20 years old tomorrow."

**Math Note**

❶ **Probability** Data and probability are usually linked together as topics in the elementary grades, but it is not until much later that students actually learn the principles and techniques that link data and probability. In Grades 4 and 5, students study the beginning building blocks of probability—how mathematics can be used to quantify likelihood in certain situations.

What word do you think we should put at the other end of our Likelihood Line? We need a word that will describe events that you are absolutely sure will happen.

Make a list of possibilities, and decide as a class which one to put on the Likelihood Line. *Certain* is a logical choice, but students may suggest words or phrases that have more meaning for them, such as *definite, going to happen, 100% sure,* and so on. Throughout these activities, we will use the word *certain* to describe the far right end of the Likelihood Line. If your students come up with an alternate word or phrase that you would like to use, just substitute that term.

Can you think of any events in the future that you are certain—absolutely sure—will happen?

Beneath the word *certain,* write down the events students suggest. Again, emphasize that you are looking for future events. Although the statement "It is certain that I am talking" may be true, it does not describe a future event. On the other hand, "It is certain that I will have a birthday next April 24" does describe a future event and therefore meets the criterion.

Making predictions gets more difficult when we start thinking about events that fall somewhere between the points marked *impossible* and *certain,* so we'll need some words to describe the middle ground.

Indicate the approximate midpoint of the Likelihood Line.

For an event located in the middle here, we would not be surprised if it happened or if it didn't happen. What word should we put here?

Again, students will suggest a variety of words or phrases. As a class, you'll need to pick one that describes a middling probability and add it to the Likelihood Line. (Throughout these activities, we will use the word *maybe* to describe the midpoint of the Likelihood Line. Some alternatives your students might suggest are *as often as not* or *even chance.*) Ask students for one or two events to write under *maybe.* Students will generate more events that match each word or phrase on the Likelihood Line in the next activity.

Indicate the approximate midpoints between *maybe* and *certain* and between *impossible* and *maybe.*

Let's add two more words or phrases to the Likelihood Line. What should we call these points on the line?

Discuss the possibilities. Label the line with words or phrases that your students agree on. These should be similar in meaning to *likely* and *unlikely,* which will be used in these activities. Other possible terms for *likely* are *good chance* and *probable,* and terms for *unlikely* may include *low chance* and *not often.*

The completed Likelihood Line may look something like this:

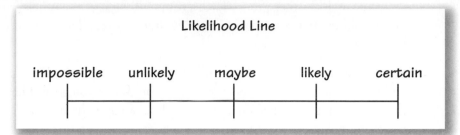

Next, suggest a few ordinary events and ask students to determine where they might go on the line. For example:

- It will snow here on Friday.

- The principal will visit our classroom this week.

- At least one student in the class will be absent tomorrow.

- The sun will come up tomorrow. ❷

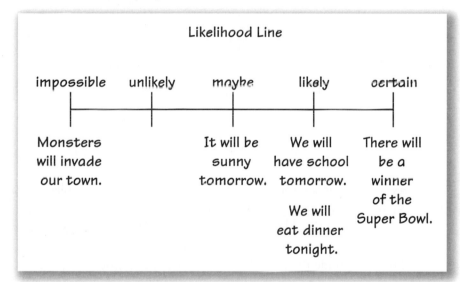

### ACTIVITY

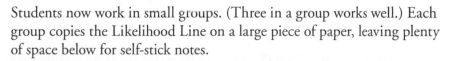

## 2 Creating Events for the Likelihood Line

30 MIN  GROUPS

Students now work in small groups. (Three in a group works well.) Each group copies the Likelihood Line on a large piece of paper, leaving plenty of space below for self-stick notes.

In your groups, you're going to think of two events for each of the five categories on the Likelihood Line and write them on self-stick notes.

---

**Teaching Note**

❷ **Certainty** Some students may argue that nothing is absolutely certain or impossible. For example, it is possible that the world will blow up today, in which case the sun would *not* come up tomorrow. If students get carried away with these kinds of objections, let them know that some events are close enough to certain or to impossible to justify using those words, given what we know about the world.

## Math Note

❸ **Personal Experience** Note that students' reasoning about the likelihood of events must be based on their own experiences. Many aspects of the context of students' lives are relevant to their judgments; therefore, which events are likely or unlikely may vary considerably from one school to another, from one class to another, and from one student to another.

You'll make an answer key and then trade your self-stick notes and your key with another group. Each group will look at the other group's events and try to place them on the Likelihood Line. Then check the key to see whether you agree.

Students write each event they come up with on a separate self-stick note and place it on the Likelihood Line under the chosen category. They then create an answer key on a separate piece of paper, listing where the events belong.

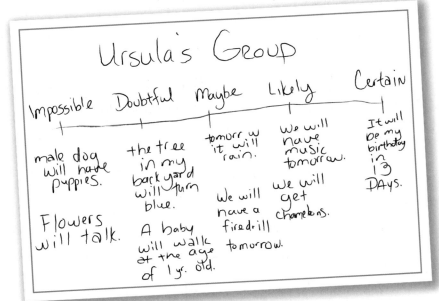

*Sample Student Work*

As students finish, they mix up their self-stick notes, and place them on an envelope and then put their answer key (folded, so that the answers are not visible) inside the envelope. Alternately, they can stick all the notes onto a plain sheet of paper along with the folded answer key. They then trade their set of events with another group.

Each group puts the new set of events on their own Likelihood Line in the categories that make sense to them. When the group is satisfied with the way they have organized the events on the line, they open the answer key and see whether their arrangement matches that of the group that brainstormed the events.

If you disagree with another group's placement of an event, write the event and where you think it should go on a sheet of paper. We'll discuss different points of view when everyone is finished.❸

If there is time, self-stick notes can be mixed up again and the envelopes traded between different groups.

## DIFFERENTIATION: Supporting the Range of Learners

**ELL** The language-based nature of this activity may pose challenges for English Language Learners. You may wish to meet with English Language Learners ahead of time to help them prepare some ideas in English that they can then exchange with their group. Students may elect to use drawings instead of words to convey their ideas.

## ONGOING ASSESSMENT: Observing Students at Work

Students create a set of events for a Likelihood Line, with two events for each category: impossible, unlikely, maybe, likely, and certain. Groups exchange sets of events and place the new set on their own Likelihood Line.

- **Can students classify events in terms of how likely they are to occur?**

- **Can students compare events and reason about which are more and less likely, judging from their own experiences?**

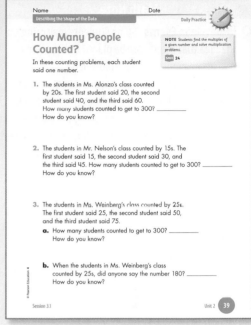
▲ Student Activity Book, p. 39

## DISCUSSION

**3**

10 MIN   CLASS

# Characterizing Events from Impossible to Certain

## Math Focus Points for Discussion

◆ Arranging events along a line representing the range of *certain* to *impossible*

For this discussion, ask students to locate the pieces of paper on which they wrote any differences of opinion from the previous activity, to use during the discussion.

Look at any events you wrote down that you think should be placed differently. What events did you write down? Where do you think they should be placed on the Likelihood Line?

Encourage students to explain their reasoning. Also ask the group that created the event to share their own reasoning. Remind them to disagree respectfully. It is easier to hear, "I disagree with your answer" or "Why did you put it in this category?" than "That's the wrong category!"

## Math Note

**❹ In-between Events** Some students may bring up the idea that events can be placed between any two of the points you have labeled on the Likelihood Line. They might see an event as not just likely, but highly likely (almost certain, but not quite). Ask them for their reasoning behind this placement. They are noticing an important idea—that probability varies along a continuum from impossible to certain and that events might fall anywhere along that continuum.

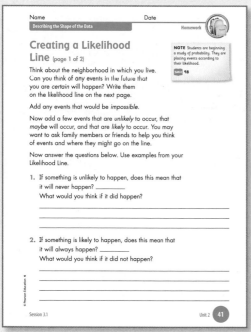

▲ Student Activity Book, p. 41

During the discussion, ask questions such as the following:

- How did you decide which category to put an event in?

- How did you decide the difference between an event in the *maybe* category and an event in the *unlikely* category (or between the *impossible* category and the *unlikely* category)?❹

- Who has a good example of an event that you'd say has a 50-50 chance of happening, one that has as good a chance of happening as not happening? Why do you think that fits in this category?

- Who has a good example of an event that isn't certain, but is more likely to happen than not to happen?

Keep the class Likelihood Line posted for the next session.

### SESSION FOLLOW-UP

# Daily Practice and Homework

 **Daily Practice:** For ongoing review, have students complete *Student Activity Book* page 39.

 **Homework:** Students place future events having to do with their neighborhoods on a Likelihood Line on *Student Activity Book* pages 41–42. Some examples may be helpful to prepare students for this homework. Discuss with students how it is unlikely that your street will be renamed this week, or how it is likely that the garbage will be picked up this week at your house.

 **Student Math Handbook:** Students and families may use *Student Math Handbook* page 98 for reference and review. See pages 154–157 in the back of this unit.

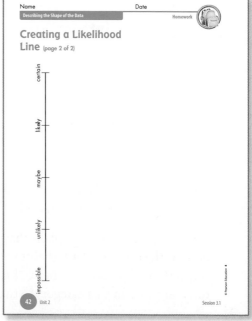

▲ Student Activity Book, p. 42

# Numerical Measures of Probability

## Math Focus Points

◆ Using numbers from 0 to 1 as measures of probability

◆ Associating verbal descriptions of probability with numeric descriptions

◆ Arranging events along a line representing the range of *certain* to *impossible*

### Vocabulary

**probability**

| Today's Plan | | Materials |
|---|---|---|
| **① DISCUSSION** **Neighborhood Events** | 10 MIN · CLASS | • *Student Activity Book,* pp. 41–42 (from Session 3.1) |
| **② ACTIVITY** **Introducing Using Numbers as Measures of Probability** | 20 MIN · CLASS · PAIRS | • Likelihood Line (from Session 3.1); paper bag or other opaque container*; colored cubes |
| **③ ACTIVITY** **Placing Events on a Likelihood Line** | 30 MIN · PAIRS | • *Student Activity Book,* pp. 43–44 • Number cubes |
| **④ SESSION FOLLOW-UP** **Daily Practice and Homework** | | • *Student Activity Book,* pp. 45–46 • *Student Math Handbook,* p. 99 |

*See *Materials to Prepare,* p. 93.

## Ten-Minute Math

*Today's Number: Broken Calculator*  Students create five expressions that equal 639. They must use only addition in their expressions. The 0, 3 and 9 keys are broken. Have two or three students give their answers as equations and explain how they know they are correct. (Examples: $151 + 488 = 639$ or $222 + 417 = 639$)

# DISCUSSION
# ① Neighborhood Events

## Math Focus Points for Discussion

◆ Arranging points along a line representing the range of *certain* to *impossible*

Ask students to share some of the events they put on their neighborhood Likelihood Line for homework (*Student Activity Book*, pages 41–42). Ask for some examples from each category. As time permits, follow up with questions such as these:

• Were examples for some categories harder to think of?

• Are there any examples that you weren't sure where to place?

20 MIN  CLASS  PAIRS

# ACTIVITY
# ② Introducing Using Numbers as Measures of Probability

Use the example of pulling a colored cube out of a container to introduce the idea that mathematicians have a way of using numbers to describe probabilities. Put one red cube and one blue cube in a bag.

I have one red cube and one blue cube in this bag. I'm going to reach in and pull one of them out. Before I do, I'm going to shake them up in the bag, so I don't know which is which. Since they're the same shape, I can't tell them apart by feeling them. So I'm just going to reach in and pull one out. What's the probability that I'm going to pull out a red cube? Think of the words we've been using—*certain, impossible, maybe, likely, unlikely.* How likely do you think it is that I'm going to pull out a red cube?

Allow pairs of students to discuss what they think for a few minutes, and then collect their ideas. Students will probably agree that it is neither certain nor impossible to pull out a red cube. Some students may bring up the idea that the chance of pulling a red cube is 1 out of 2. Others may not be convinced that pulling a red cube and pulling a blue cube are equally likely. It is not necessary for everyone to agree that the probability is 1 out of 2 in order to continue the discussion, so go on after a few minutes to introduce putting numbers on the Likelihood Line.

When we made this Likelihood Line, we came up with some words to describe probabilities. Mathematicians use numbers instead of words to describe the probability of an event. Some of you agree that the probability of pulling out a red cube is the same as the probability of pulling out a blue cube. If that is true—if there is an even chance—what number do you think mathematicians might use for the probability of pulling out a red cube?

Students may have good reasons for suggesting a variety of numbers. Students may have heard probabilities expressed as percents (for example, a 50 percent chance of rain) or may have heard the expression "a 50–50 chance" to describe an event that is just as likely to happen as not, so they might choose 50. Explain that mathematicians decided to use the number $\frac{1}{2}$ to describe a probability like this one.

Mathematicians have agreed to assign $\frac{1}{2}$ to what we were calling *maybe* on our Likelihood Line. They say that *impossible* is a probability of 0 and *certain* is a probability of 1.

Write 0 under *impossible*, $\frac{1}{2}$ under *maybe*, and 1 under *certain*. You may also decide to write 50 percent under *maybe* if it is brought up.

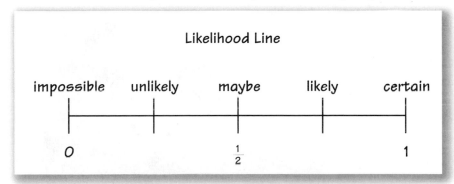

So if the probability of an event is $\frac{1}{2}$, there is a 1 out of 2 or $\frac{1}{2}$ chance that the event will happen. These are just some of the probabilities we could write on this line. There could be many other fractions between *maybe* and *certain* and between *maybe* and *impossible*.

Before students work on problems on their own, ask them to work on one more problem.

Now I'm going to put 2 red cubes and 6 blue cubes in my bag and shake them up. What's the probability that I'm going to pull out a red cube now? Is it close to a half, close to 0, close to 1? About where would you place it on our Likelihood Line?

Students again work in pairs for a few minutes on this problem. Then ask students to share their reasoning about where they would put the probability of pulling out a red cube on the Likelihood Line. This problem presents a situation in which there is not an equal chance of each of two

## Math Note

❶ **Two Aspects to Probability** Do not expect all students to be able to name the exact probability of pulling a red cube out of the bag in the 2 out of 8 situation yet. Use this example as a way to establish the idea that there are two aspects of a situation to consider when talking about probability: the number of possible outcomes (e.g., 8 different cubes) and the number of possibilities for a particular outcome (e.g., 2 red cubes).

## Professional Development

❷ **Dialogue Box:** Discussing Probability Experiments, p. 152

possibilities occurring. Because there are 8 possibilities (8 different cubes) and 2 of them are red, there is a 2 out of 8 chance that a red cube will be chosen, assuming there is an equal chance of pulling any cube out of the bag. This probability can be expressed as 2 out of 8 ($\frac{2}{8}$), or 1 out of 4 ($\frac{1}{4}$), or 25 percent.❶

As they work through problems in this session and the next, ask students to use the cubes to demonstrate what fraction a certain color is of the total number of cubes.❷

Focus the discussion on where on the Likelihood Line the students would place the chance of pulling out a red cube in this situation. Even if they can't describe the probability as a specific fraction, ask questions to help them think about whether the probability is close to $\frac{1}{2}$, less than $\frac{1}{2}$, or more than $\frac{1}{2}$.

*Working with physical objects makes it easier for students to understand probability.*

When we had only two cubes, you said that there was an even chance of pulling out red or blue. Now with 2 red and 6 blue, is it as likely that I'll pull out a red cube as a blue? Less likely or more likely?

Emphasize to students that assigning a probability to an event is a way of capturing likelihood, but it does not predict the future. That is, although in this situation it is *less likely* that a red cube will be pulled out of the bag than a blue, the assigned probability of $\frac{1}{4}$ does not predict exactly when a red cube might be pulled out. The hand reaching into the bag does not know which cube it is touching.

The assigned probability indicates that, over time, it is likely that a red cube will be pulled out about one out of every four times, but that does not mean that there will be one red cube and three blue cubes in each successive group of four.❸

**Professional Development**

❸ **Teacher Note:** Impossible, Certain, and Everything in Between, p. 134

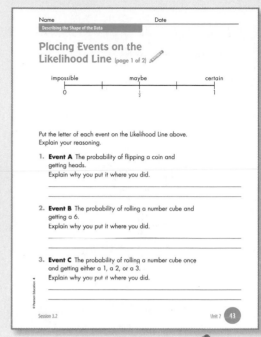

**ACTIVITY**

# ③ Placing Events on a Likelihood Line

**30 MIN   PAIRS**

Have students work in pairs on *Student Activity Book* pages 43–44 to describe numerically the probability of some events. Ask students to place the letter of each event on the spot that corresponds to the probability of its happening. Remind students that they can use the entire Likelihood Line, not just the five points that are labeled.

Note that on page 43, a *number cube* refers to a standard number cube with six faces, labeled with the numbers 1 through 6.

*Students learn to figure the probability of different events.*

As students work, circulate to find out how students are determining the probabilities of the events and why they think each event goes in a particular place on the Likelihood Line. Some students may be able to use specific fractions to describe the probabilities of the events, but others may describe the probabilities as "more than $\frac{1}{2}$," "close to 1," and so on.

## ✓ ONGOING ASSESSMENT: Observing Students at Work

Students place events on a number line that indicates probability from 0 to 1.

---

**Placing Events on the Likelihood Line** (page 1 of 2)

impossible       maybe       certain

0                 $\frac{1}{2}$                 1

Put the letter of each event on the Likelihood Line above. Explain your reasoning.

1. **Event A** The probability of flipping a coin and getting heads.
Explain why you put it where you did.

2. **Event B** The probability of rolling a number cube and getting a 6.
Explain why you put it where you did.

3. **Event C** The probability of rolling a number cube once and getting either a 1, a 2, or a 3.
Explain why you put it where you did.

▲ Student Activity Book, p. 43

**Placing Events on the Likelihood Line** (page 2 of 2)

4. **Event D** the probability of pulling a blue cube out of a bag that contains 1 red cube and 99 blue cubes.
Explain why you put it where you did.

5. **Event E** the probability of pulling a girl's name out of a container that holds the names of all of the students in the class.
Explain why you put it where you did.

6. **Event F** the probability of pulling a boy's name out of the same container.
Explain why you put it where you did.

7. **Event G** the probability of pulling your name out of the same container.
Explain why you put it where you did.

▲ Student Activity Book, p. 44

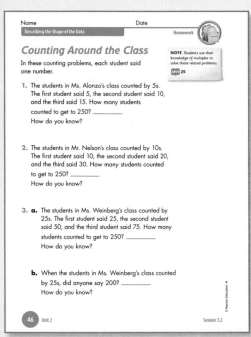

▲ Student Activity Book, p. 45

▲ Student Activity Book, p. 46

- Can students decide on where to place an event on the number line?

- For which events can students choose an exact fraction to describe the probability of the event?

## DIFFERENTIATION: Supporting the Range of Learners

**Intervention** Refer students who are having difficulty determining the numerical probability of events back to the Likelihood Line that used only words to describe the probability of events on *Student Activity Book* page 42 *(impossible, unlikely, maybe, likely, or certain)*. Ask them to place events on this line first. Then use $\frac{1}{2}$ as a landmark to help them think about placing these events on the Likelihood Line with fractions. For example, for Problems 2 and 3 on *Student Activity Book* page 43, is there an equal chance of rolling a 6, or is it more likely that a 1, 2, or 3 will be rolled? Keep the focus on placing the events according to their relationship to $\frac{1}{2}$ (an *even chance*) or to 1 *(certainty)*.

**Intervention** Students who are having difficulty describing the probability of any of the events in words can work on trying out the situation in Problems 2 and 3—rolling a number cube and getting a 6, or getting a 1, 2, or 3. They should roll the number cube 40 times (or more) and keep track of what they roll. After they record 40 or so rolls, they can compare the situations. How many times did they roll a 6? How many times did they roll a 1, 2, or 3? Why do they think that occurred? Then they can alter the experiment, using a bag with 2 red cubes and 6 blue cubes. Although all students will be carrying out experiments like this one in the next session, some students can benefit from trying this a number of times.

### SESSION FOLLOW-UP

## Daily Practice and Homework

**Daily Practice:** For ongoing review, have students complete *Student Activity Book* page 45.

**Homework:** Students solve multiplication story problems based on Counting Around the Class on *Student Activity Book* page 46.

**Student Math Handbook:** Students and families may use *Student Math Handbook* page 99 for reference and review. See pages 154–157 in the back of this unit.

# Probability Experiments

## Math Focus Points

◆ Comparing the expected probability of an event with the actual results of repeated trials of that event

◆ Arranging events along a line representing the range of *certain* to *impossible*

◆ Using numbers from 0 to 1 as measures of probability

| Today's Plan | | Materials |
|---|---|---|
| **DISCUSSION** **1 What's the Probability?** 20 MIN CLASS | | • *Student Activity Book,* pp. 43–44 (from Session 3.2) • Number cube; Likelihood Line (from Session 3.1); self-stick notes |
| **ACTIVITY** **2 Probability Experiments** 40 MIN PAIRS | | • *Student Activity Book,* p. 47 • M17* • Blank 0–50 line plot*; clear container with cubes*; chart paper; paper bag or other opaque container; red and blue cubes |
| **SESSION FOLLOW-UP** **3 Daily Practice** | | • *Student Activity Book,* p. 48 • *Student Math Handbook,* pp. 99–100 |

*See *Materials to Prepare,* p. 93.

## Ten-Minute Math

***Quick Survey*** For the survey, ask the class, "How many kinds of fruits and vegetables did you eat yesterday?" or a different numerical question that you or the students choose. Make sure that the data they collect is something they already know or can observe easily and is likely to change on a different day. Keep the class data for comparison in the next session. With today's data, make a line plot. Ask the following:

• What do you notice about the data?

• What does the data tell us about our class?

# ① What's the Probability?

## Math Focus Points for Discussion

◆ Arranging events along a line representing the range of *certain* to *impossible*

◆ Using numbers from 0 to 1 as measures of probability

Ask students where they placed the seven events on the Likelihood Line on *Student Activity Book* pages 43–44. Then, focus on a few of the problems. Ask questions to elicit students' reasoning about their choices.

What is one event that you decided had a probability of $\frac{1}{2}$? Why do you think the probability is $\frac{1}{2}$?

### Students might say:

"There's a 1 out of 2 chance when you flip a fair coin. There are two possibilities—heads and tails—so getting heads is one of those two possibilities."

"The probability is also $\frac{1}{2}$ for getting a 1, 2, or 3 if you roll a number cube."

Who can explain how that works?

Help students articulate how many possibilities there are in each situation (e.g., 6 faces on the cube), and how many of those are being considered (1, 2, and 3—3 of the faces). The measure of probability ($\frac{3}{6}$ or $\frac{1}{2}$) expresses the number of possibilities being considered out of the total number of possible outcomes.

Looking at the probability of several different outcomes is a new idea for many students. If you noticed that Event C, the probability of rolling a number cube once and getting either a 1, 2, or 3, was difficult for students to understand, spend some time demonstrating how you would collect data about Event C. Roll a number cube and collect data, using a table like this one.

| Number rolled | 1, 2, 3? |
|:---:|:---:|
| 1 | yes |
| 5 | no |
| 6 | no |
| 2 | yes |
| 5 | no |
| 4 | no |
| 3 | yes |

Choose one or two of the other problems to discuss. For these problems, first ask students to give an approximate position on the number line—whether the probability is 0, $\frac{1}{2}$, 1, between 0 and $\frac{1}{2}$, or between $\frac{1}{2}$ and 1. Ask students whether they decided on a number to represent the probability and why. If others disagree with the probability, ask them to share their reasoning. After the probability has been agreed on, have a student write the event on a stick-on note and place it on the class Likelihood Line.

Close the discussion by asking whether anyone can express the exact probability for Event D—pulling a blue cube out of a bag that contains 1 red cube and 99 blue cubes. It is probably clear to students that the probability is very close to 1. What fraction can express this probability?

## ACTIVITY
## ② Probability Experiments

40 MIN   PAIRS

Post the blank 0–50 line plot in a place where students can record on it.

During the last session, you determined the probability of pulling a red cube out of a bag that had 1 red cube and 1 blue cube. What did you determine the probability to be? (*$\frac{1}{2}$ or 1 out of 2*)

Hold up the clear container with cubes.

I have 10 red cubes and 10 blue cubes in this container.

Ask students some of the following questions.

• What is the probability of my pulling a red cube out of the jar?

• What is the probability of my pulling a blue cube out of the jar? Why do you think so?

## Professional Development

**❶ Teacher Note:** Impossible, Certain, and Everything in Between, p. 134

## Math Note

**❷ Understanding Probability** Some students may realize that although the probability of pulling out either color is $\frac{1}{2}$ on any one trial, this does not mean that out of 50 trials they will pull out exactly 25 red and 25 blue cubes. They may reason, however, that the result will probably be half red, half blue. Other students may think that it will be exactly 25 times, and still others may not have a good idea about what will happen. This experiment will be an opportunity to test out their predictions and compare them with the expected probability.

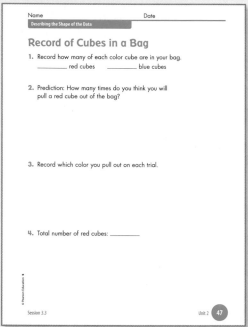

▲ **Student Activity Book, p. 47**
**Resource Masters, M17**

- Suppose I do this 50 times. Each time I record which color I pull out and then put the cube back. [Demonstrate this.] In a few minutes you will have a chance to try this experiment yourself.

- What is your prediction for what will actually happen when you try this?

- What if each pair tries this? Will everyone get the same results?

Write some predictions on chart paper or on the board.❶ Label the list "Experiment 1," and save it for Session 3.4.❷

Ask students to look at *Student Activity Book* page 47. Each pair of students shares a bag with 10 red cubes and 10 blue cubes. One student pulls out a cube while the other records whether the cube is red or blue. Then students switch roles. Point out that they need to write the number of cubes they have in their bag (e.g., 10 red cubes and 10 blue cubes) as well as their prediction for what will happen before they start.

Each pair should decide beforehand how they will record their results. Some students keep track by listing the numbers 1–50 and writing an R or B next to each number as they go along. Others use tally marks. Emphasize that their method should allow them to determine when they have pulled out a cube exactly 50 times.

Remind students not to look as they pull a cube out, to record the color of the cube, to replace the cube before drawing another one so that there are always 20 cubes in the bag, and to shake the bag.

When students finish drawing cubes and recording, they count how many red cubes were pulled out of the bag. Then each pair puts an X over that number on the posted 0–50 line plot.

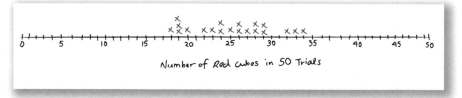

As students finish, they should work on Experiment 2, the same as the first but with 5 red cubes and 15 blue cubes in the bag. They record their work on a copy of Record of Cubes in a Bag (M17). If quite a few students are ready to move on to the 5 red/15 blue cube experiment, you may want to stop the class and introduce this experiment, even if not all students are finished with the first experiment. Again, ask students to make predictions: out of 50 tries, about how many red cubes do they expect to pull out of the bag? Label this list of predictions "Experiment 2," and save it for Session 3.4.

As students finish the second experiment, they use a different symbol to record the number of red cubes each pair drew out of the 5 red/15 blue bag on the line plot.

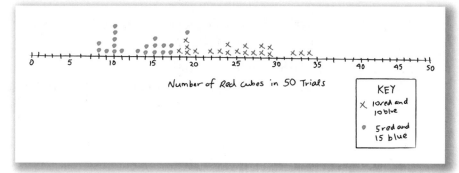

Students will have time to finish these experiments in the next session.

## ONGOING ASSESSMENT: Observing Students at Work

Students collect data on the number of times a red cube is pulled out of a bag containing red and blue cubes.

- **Can students make a reasonable prediction for the number of times they will pull a red cube out of the bag?** Can they explain the reasoning behind their prediction?

- **Do students figure out what the expected probability of pulling out one color is (e.g., $\frac{1}{2}$ for pulling a red cube out of a bag with 10 red cubes and 10 blue cubes)?** Do they distinguish between what happens theoretically and what happens in an actual experiment?

- **Can students record and keep track of the data they collect?**

## DIFFERENTIATION: Supporting the Range of Learners

**Intervention** Think about how to set up partnerships to support students who might have difficulty keeping track of their data. Talk with students about what will help them keep track.

**Extension** Some students may be curious about what would happen if they ran their experiment again. After they have posted their data on the class line plot, encourage them to carry out another 50 trials with half red and half blue. They can add the result from this new experiment to the class line plot.

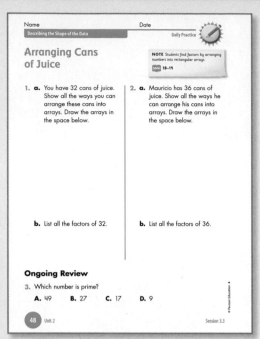

Name _____ Date _____

Describing the Shape of the Data                    Daily Practice

## Arranging Cans of Juice

NOTE Students find factors by arranging numbers into rectangular arrays.

Skill 18–19

1. **a.** You have 32 cans of juice. Show all the ways you can arrange these cans into arrays. Draw the arrays in the space below.

   2. **a.** Mauricio has 36 cans of juice. Show all the ways he can arrange his cans into arrays. Draw the arrays in the space below.

   **b.** List all the factors of 32.

   **b.** List all the factors of 36.

## Ongoing Review

3. Which number is prime?

   **A.** 49      **B.** 27      **C.** 17      **D.** 9

48  Unit 2                                    Session 3.3

▲ **Student Activity Book p. 48**

## SESSION FOLLOW-UP

# ③ Daily Practice

**Daily Practice:** For ongoing review, have students complete *Student Activity Book* page 48.

**Student Math Handbook:** Students and families may use *Student Math Handbook* pages 99–100 for reference and review. See pages 154–157 in the back of this unit.

# Comparing Probability Experiments

## Math Focus Points

◆ Comparing the expected probability of an event with the actual results of repeated trials of that event

◆ Comparing two sets of data by using the shape and spread of the data

| Today's Plan | | Materials |
|---|---|---|
| **ACTIVITY** **①** **Probability Experiments** | 🕐 25 MIN  👥 PAIRS | • *Student Activity Book*, pp. 49–50 (optional) • M17 (as needed) • Paper bag or other opaque container; red and blue cubes; class line plot (from Session 3.3) |
| **DISCUSSION** **②** **Comparing the Three Experiments** | 🕐 35 MIN  👥 CLASS  🧍 INDIVIDUALS | • *Student Activity Book*, pp. 49–50 • Lists of predictions (from Session 3.3) |
| **SESSION FOLLOW-UP** **③** **Daily Practice** | | • *Student Activity Book*, p. 51 • *Student Math Handbook*, pp. 99–100 |

## Ten-Minute Math

*Quick Survey*  For the survey, collect data about the same question you used in the previous session (How many kinds of fruits and vegetables did you eat yesterday?). Add today's data to the line plot created in the last session and ask students to make comparisons. Ask:

- What do you notice about our data today?
- How are the data the same as last session's?
- How are they different?
- What does that tell us about our class?

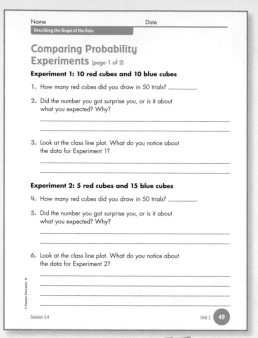

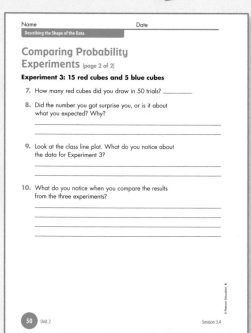

▲ **Student Activity Book, p. 49** PORTFOLIO

▲ **Student Activity Book, p. 50** PORTFOLIO

25 MIN   PAIRS

### ACTIVITY

# 1 Probability Experiments

Students continue working on their probability experiments. If possible, each pair should complete three experiments. Students will need another copy of Record of Cubes in a Bag (M17) to record their work for Experiment 3.

Experiment 1: 50 trials of pulling 1 cube from a container of 10 red cubes and 10 blue cubes

Experiment 2: 50 trials of pulling 1 cube from a container of 5 red cubes and 15 blue cubes

Experiment 3: 50 trials of pulling 1 cube from a container of 15 red cubes and 5 blue cubes

Before pairs begin, ask students to predict the outcome of Experiment 3. Make a list of predictions and label the list Experiment 3. Post it with the lists of predictions for Experiment 1 and Experiment 2 from Session 3.3.

In each case, the students count up the number of red cubes. Then each pair records their results on the class line plot. You need to designate a different symbol for each of the three experiments so that they can be distinguished on the line plot.

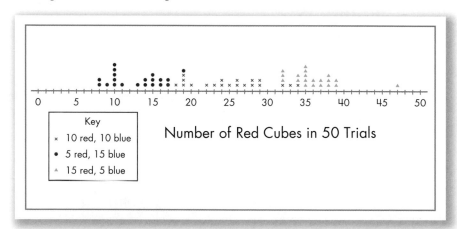

Number of Red Cubes in 50 Trials

Key
× 10 red, 10 blue
• 5 red, 15 blue
▲ 15 red, 5 blue

Students who finish all three experiments can begin work on *Student Activity Book* pages 49–50.

## ONGOING ASSESSMENT: Observing Students at Work

Students collect data on the number of times a red cube is pulled out of a bag containing red and blue cubes. They complete three experiments: one with 10 red and 10 blue cubes, one with 5 red and 15 blue cubes, and one with 15 red and 5 blue cubes.

See Session 3.3, page 111 for things to look for while observing students.

### DISCUSSION

# Comparing the Three Experiments

35 MIN   CLASS   INDIVIDUALS

## Math Focus Points for Discussion

◆ Comparing the expected probability of an event with the actual results of repeated trials of that event

◆ Comparing two sets of data by using the shape and spread of the data

Draw students' attention to the list of their predictions for Experiment 1 from Session 3.3: how many times they would pull out a red cube in 50 tries in the 10 red/10 blue experiment. Ask them to look at the predictions and at the data on the line plot.

In Experiment 1, you had 10 red cubes and 10 blue cubes in your bag. How do the results of pulling a cube out of that bag compare with your predictions?

Students may point out that there was a range of results, but that many of their predictions fit within the range of results. Ask students about how this range of results compares with a prediction of choosing a red cube 25 times.

Many of you predicted that if you pulled out a cube 50 times, you'd get red 25 times. Why did you make that prediction? Does it surprise you that everybody didn't get 25 red cubes?

Most students will probably understand that although 25 is the most reasonable prediction, it does not always work out that exactly 25 cubes are red.

Next ask students to look at the data for Experiment 2 and Experiment 3 and to compare these results with the results for Experiment 1.

How do the data from the three different experiments compare? How do the results compare with your predictions?

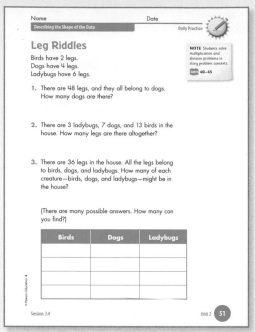

**▲ Student Activity Book, p. 51**

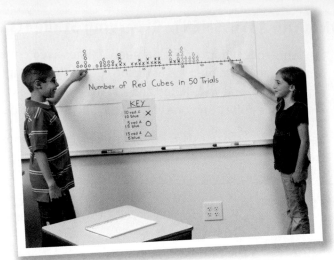

*Students notice how data clump together.*

Students will notice that most or all the data for Experiment 2 show an outcome of fewer than 25 red cubes, that the data from Experiment 1 show around 25 red cubes, and that the data from Experiment 3 show more than 25 red cubes. Most students probably made predictions that are within the data results.

At the end of the discussion, students work individually on *Student Activity Book* pages 49–50.

**SESSION FOLLOW-UP**

# ③ Daily Practice

 **Daily Practice:** For ongoing review, have students complete *Student Activity Book* page 51.

 **Student Math Handbook:** Students and families may use *Student Math Handbook* pages 99–100 for reference and review. See pages 154–157 in the back of this unit.

# End-of-Unit Assessment

## Math Focus Points

◆ Describing the shape of a data set: where the data are spread out or concentrated, what the highest and lowest values are, range is, and what the outliers are

◆ Comparing two sets of data by using the shape and spread of the data

◆ Developing arguments based on the data

◆ Arranging events along a line representing the range of *certain* to *impossible*

◆ Using numbers from 0 to 1 as measures of probability

| Today's Plan | | Materials |
|---|---|---|
| **ASSESSMENT ACTIVITY** **① End-of-Unit Assessment** | ✓ 🕐 👤 60 MIN  INDIVIDUALS | • M6 (optional), M18–M21* |
| **SESSION FOLLOW-UP** **② Daily Practice** | | • *Student Activity Book,* p. 52 • *Student Math Handbook,* pp. 94–98 |

*See *Materials to Prepare,* p. 93.

## Ten-Minute Math

*Today's Number: Broken Calculator*  Students create five expressions that equal 2,874. They must use only subtraction in their expressions. The 2, 6, and 8 keys are broken. Have two or three students give their answers as equations and explain how they know they are correct. (Examples: $3,974 - 1,100 = 2,874$ or $5,000 - 1,459 - 557 - 110 = 2,874$)

## Professional Development

❶ **Teacher Note:** End-of-Unit Assessment, p. 136

❷ Assessment in this Unit, p. 15

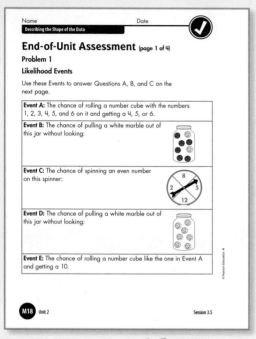

▲ **Resource Masters, M18** PORTFOLIO

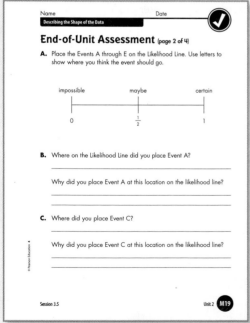

▲ **Resource Masters, M19** PORTFOLIO

**ASSESSMENT ACTIVITY**

# ① End-of-Unit Assessment

60 MIN  INDIVIDUALS

This End-of-Unit Assessment (M18–M21) focuses on three of the unit's benchmarks.❶ ❷

Problem 1 assesses Benchmark 6: Describe the likelihood of an event in terms of a scale from impossible (probability of 0) to certain (probability of 1). For Problem 1, students place five events on a Likelihood Line. They explain why they placed two of the events at the locations they chose. Make sure that students understand that they are to put the letters of the five events, A–E, on the Likelihood Line.

Problem 2 assesses Benchmark 3: Describe the shape of the data from a numerical data set, including where the data are concentrated and the highest, lowest, and median values. Problem 2 also assesses Benchmark 4: Use data to compare two groups. For this problem, students describe and compare the temperatures in Boston and Philadelphia during July. They interpret a line plot showing a set of temperatures for July in Philadelphia. Then they make a line plot of a set of temperatures for the same month in Boston and compare the two data sets.

## SESSION FOLLOW-UP

# Daily Practice

 **Daily Practice:** For enrichment, have students complete *Student Activity Book* page 52.

**Student Math Handbook:** Students and families may use *Student Math Handbook* pages 94–98 for reference and review. See pages 154–157 in the back of this unit.

▲ **Student Activity Book, p. 52**

---

Name _____ Date _____
Describing the Shape of the Data ✓

### End-of-Unit Assessment (page 3 of 4)

**Problem 2**

**Was It Hotter in Philadelphia or Boston?**

Samantha is thinking about moving to either Philadelphia or Boston. She wants to know what the average temperature is in each city because she does not like really hot weather. Here is a line plot of the recorded high temperatures for every day of July, 2003, in Philadelphia. The temperatures are in degrees Fahrenheit.

71 72 73 74 75 76 77 78 79 80 81 82 83 84 85 86 87 88 89 90 91 92 93 94 95

**Recorded high temperatures in degrees Fahrenheit for each day in July, 2003**

**A.** Describe to Samantha the temperature in Philadelphia in July, 2003, based on the data in this line plot. Consider where the data are concentrated, what the highest and lowest temperatures are, and what the outliers and the median are as you write your comparison. Write at least three statements about the temperature in Philadelphia in July, 2003.

_____
_____
_____
_____
_____

**M20** Unit 2                                    Session 3.5

▲ **Resource Masters, M20**

---

Name _____ Date _____
Describing the Shape of the Data ✓

### End-of-Unit Assessment (page 4 of 4)

Here are the recorded high temperatures for every day of July, 2003, in Boston. The temperatures are in degrees Fahrenheit:

83  80  81  89  93  93  81  91  81  72
66  85  85  78  82  81  76  84  84  85
82  82  86  88  89  84  77  82  73

**B.** Make a line plot of the temperatures in Boston in July, 2003, on a separate piece of paper.

**C.** What can you tell Samantha about how the temperature in Boston in July compared with the temperature in Philadelphia? Write at least three statements that compare the temperatures in the two cities in July. Consider where the data are concentrated, what the highest and lowest temperatures are, any outliers, and what the medians are as you write your comparison.

_____
_____
_____

**D.** According to these data, would you tell Samantha that July, 2003, was a hotter month in Boston or in Philadelphia? Use the data to support your answer.

_____
_____

Session 3.5                              Unit 2 **M21**

▲ **Resource Masters, M21**

# Describing the Shape of the Data: Data Analysis and Probability

## Teacher Notes

| | |
|---|---|
| Data Terms and Representations | 121 |
| Focusing on the Shape of the Data | 123 |
| Finding and Using the Median | 125 |
| Assessment: Comparing Numbers of Cavities | 127 |
| Numerical and Categorical Data | 130 |
| Collecting Data from Other Classes | 131 |
| About the Mystery Data | 132 |
| Impossible Certain, and Everything in Between | 134 |
| End-of-Unit Assessment | 136 |

In Part 6 of *Implementing Investigations in Grade 4*, you will find a set of Teacher Notes that addresses topics and issues applicable to the curriculum as a whole rather than to specific curriculum units. They include the following:

Computational Fluency and Place Value

Computational Algorithms and Methods

Representations and Contexts for Mathematical Work

Foundations of Algebra in the Elementary Grades

Discussing Mathematical Ideas

Racial and Linguistic Diversity in the Classroom:
  What Does Equity Mean in Today's Math Classroom?

## Dialogue Boxes

| | |
|---|---|
| Describing the Shape of the Raisin Data | 144 |
| What Is a Typical Height? | 146 |
| What Does the Median Tell You? | 147 |
| Refining a Survey Question | 149 |
| Is This a Good Game? | 151 |
| Discussing Probability Experiments | 152 |

## Student Math Handbook ....... 154

## Index ....... 158

# Teacher Note

# Data Terms and Representations

## Line Plot

Throughout this unit, line plots are used to show the frequency with which each value of the data appears. A line plot is simply a horizontal axis, with a regular scale, and with each piece of data marked as an X, as in this line plot of the number of raisins in a box.

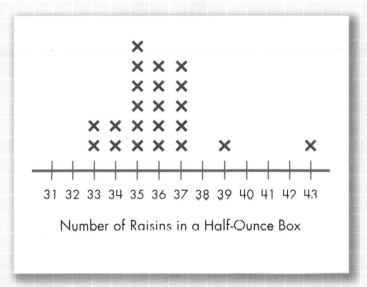

Number of Raisins in a Half-Ounce Box

In the line plot, each X stands for one piece of data. The column of Xs at each value shows the number of pieces of data with that value. In Grade 3, students sorted out the meaning of the symbols and numbers on a line plot. Some students may need help reviewing how to read this graph. For example, to describe the graph above, students might say, "There are 6 on 35" or "36 and 37 have 5." First, it is critical that teachers help students clarify what they mean by such statements. You might ask, "What do you mean, 'there are 6 on 35'? What does the 6 mean? What does the 35 mean? What does this tell us about boxes of raisins?" Students may need to spend time sorting out what these numbers mean—that 6 boxes of raisins each had 35 raisins. Students need to think through which numbers indicate a *value* of the data (e.g., 35 raisins in a box) and which numbers indicate a *frequency* (how often that value occurred in the data set; e.g., 6 boxes had that value).

Note that a *line plot* is not the same kind of graph as a *line graph*. The line graph is used to show how a variable changes continuously in relationship to another variable—for example, a graph of temperature over time. Students work with line graphs in the unit *Penny Jars and Plant Growth*.

Discussions of the shape of the data give you the opportunity to bring up statistical terms that students can use to describe the data. In particular, the terms *range, outlier, mode,* and *median* are useful for fourth graders. The first three terms were introduced in Grade 3 and should be revisited here. Introduce these terms as the ideas they represent come up in students' descriptions of the data. For information about the median, see **Teacher Note:** Finding and Using the Median, page 125.

## Range

The range of the data is technically the difference between the highest and lowest values in the data set. In the data set shown in the line plot above, the range of the data is 10, the difference between 33 and 43. Often students talk about the minimum and maximum values, rather than the distance between them, so they might say, "The data range from 33 to 43" or "The range is from 33 to 43." The range gives an indication of the spread of the data. In Session 1.2, when students make predictions about first graders' heights, they consider whether the range of first-grade heights might be different from the range of fourth-grade heights. Will fourth-grade heights be more spread out? That is, will the difference between the shortest and tallest fourth graders be greater than, less than, or about the same as the difference between the shortest and tallest first graders? See more about this question below under "Outlier."

## Mode

The mode is the value that has more data than any other value in the data set. The mode of the data set shown above is 35. There can be more than one mode in a set of data. For example, in this data set, if there were also 6 pieces of data at 37, there would be two modes.

The mode is easy for students to identify. However, in order to assess the importance of the mode, students need to think about the mode in the context of the entire data set. In this data set, there are more boxes of raisins with 35 raisins than any other number, but there are almost as many boxes with 36 and 37 raisins. What is more important in these data than the mode by itself is the larger modal clump of data from 35 to 37. More than $\frac{2}{3}$ of the data falls into this clump.

A mode can be a part of an important modal clump, or it might reveal little of importance about the data. Consider this data set, showing how many years eighth graders have been at their K–8 school.

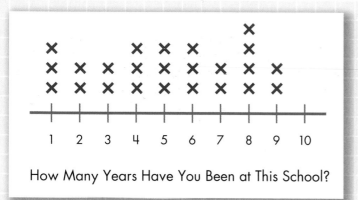

How Many Years Have You Been at This School?

There is a mode at 8 years, but the data are in general quite spread out. The mode does not indicate a particularly important concentration or cluster. A report about these data that reported the mode as an important indicator would give a misleading picture of these data. By fourth grade, students should be encouraged to move away from the mode and focus on the shape of the data—how it is concentrated and spread out. When students notice the mode, ask them how much of the data set that mode represents and whether it is part of a larger modal clump of data.

**Anna:** 8 years has the most.

**Teacher:** What do you mean, "the most"? What does that say about our class?

**Anna:** The most students have been here 8 years.

**Teacher:** And how many students is that?

**Anna:** 4. Oh, I guess that's not a lot.

The mode alone does not tell enough about the overall story of most numerical data sets, although it is one of the few statistics available for categorical data. See **Teacher Note:** Numerical and Categorical Data, page 130.

## Outlier

An outlier is a value that is much higher or much lower than other values in the data set. Statisticians have developed formulas for determining how much higher or lower a value must be in order to define it as an outlier. In this unit, students work with the idea of an outlier without having a particular mathematical rule for determining one. They look for values that are unusual and think about what might account for that value. Is it an error in the data, or is it an unusual value that might show something interesting about the data?

Including or excluding an outlier can affect the description of how the data are spread out. For example, including the outliers, the range of the raisin data above is 10 raisins—that is, one might expect a difference of as much as 10 raisins in a box. However, excluding the outlier at 43, the range is only 6, which probably more accurately represents the variation you might ordinarily expect in a box of raisins.

# Teacher Note

# Focusing on the Shape of the Data

A major goal of this unit is for students to use data to compare two groups. Mathematically, comparing two sets of data presents an interesting problem: How do you compare a set of many different values with another set of many different values? It is relatively straightforward for a fourth grader to compare two values. For example, Marisol is 4 feet 2 inches tall, and her mother is 5 feet 2 inches tall. How much taller is Marisol's mother?

But how can you compare the heights of the members of a whole group of people with the heights of the members of another group? For example, how much taller are fourth graders than first graders? This question is a different kind of question than the one about Marisol and her mother. It raises two important and complex statistical issues. First, to answer this question, we cannot measure only one first grader and one fourth grader. We will need information about many first graders and many fourth graders. Deciding how many students to measure and how to select which students to measure raises important issues about choosing a sample—questions that are not the focus of the work in this unit. What students will be focusing on is the second issue: When you have data for two groups, how can you use that data to compare?

Listing all the individual values in each data set does not move us very far toward being able to say something about how the two groups compare. Instead, the data for each group must be described as a whole, focusing on the overall shape of the data, and then summarized, highlighting the most important features of the data. What features of the data are important will depend, in part, on the particular data set. Here are several data sets showing how many years different groups of eighth graders have been at their K–8 schools.

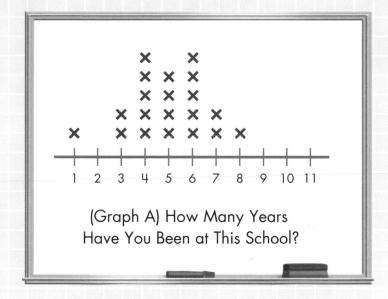

(Graph A) How Many Years
Have You Been at This School?

Sometimes there is a central clump of data in which a large proportion of the data are concentrated. In Graph A, more than half the students have been at this school for 4, 5, or 6 years.

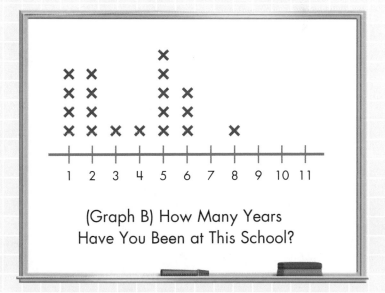

(Graph B) How Many Years
Have You Been at This School?

Sometimes there is more than one area in which data are concentrated. In Graph B, there is one group of students who have been at this school 5 or 6 years and another group that has been there only 1 or 2 years.

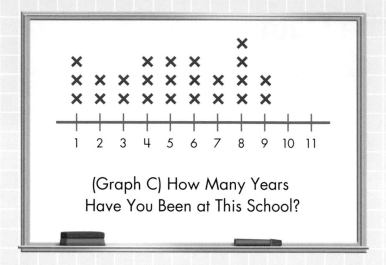

(Graph C) How Many Years
Have You Been at This School?

Sometimes data are very spread out and there is no place where they are concentrated. In Graph C, there does not seem to be a clear pattern to how many years students have been at the school.

As you discuss data with your students, help them focus on the shape of the data by asking questions like these:

• Do you see any clumps of data?

• Where are the data very spread out? Where are data clustered together?

• About how much of the class is in that clump of data? About half? More than half? Less than half?

• What values are most typical or usual in this data set? What values are unusual?

See **Teacher Note:** Data Terms and Representations, page 121, and **Teacher Note:** Finding and Using the Median, page 125, for more information about particular statistical features of data that you can review or introduce as they come up in discussion.

# Teacher Note

# Finding and Using the Median

In order to compare two or more sets of data, statisticians needed some tools to summarize a data set. (See **Teacher Note:** Focusing on the Shape of the Data, page 123.) The median is one landmark that can be used as part of a description of a set of data. For large data sets, such as housing prices in a community or census data, the median provides a relatively stable average or measure of center. For example, according to the U.S. Census Bureau, the median age in the United States in 2000 was 35.3. This statistic indicates that half the U.S. population was 35.3 years old or younger and that the other half of the population was aged 35.3 years or older. This statistic tells us that there are as many people in the first three and a half decades of life in the U.S. as there are people in all the remaining decades. The median, combined with some knowledge of the lowest and highest values, give us some sense of how the data are spread out.

The median is the midpoint of the data set. Imagine that each person in the U.S. were to write his or her age on an index card. Then we collect all the index cards and put them all in order from youngest to oldest. Finally, we find the middle card. That value is the median age. Note that if we have an odd number of cards, the median age is the value on the middle card. If we have an even number of cards, the median age is the value midway between the ages on the two middle cards.

Notice that the median is not the middle of the range of values. If the lowest age is 0 (for newborns) and the highest age is 100, the middle of this range would be 50 years. But the population is not spread evenly over this range. Just as many people are in about the first third of the range as in the last two-thirds, so the median is at age 35, not at age 50. The median is the value that equally divides all of the pieces of data.

Another example of how a median can indicate how data are spread over their range is the data set students will encounter on Assessment: Comparing Numbers of Cavities (M7–M8).

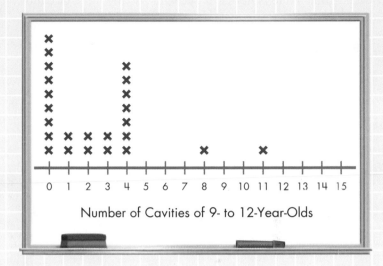

Number of Cavities of 9- to 12-Year-Olds

This line plot shows the numbers of lifetime cavities of twenty-four 9- to 12-year-olds. One way to find the median is to list all the values in order. There are 24 pieces of data, so to find the middle value, count to the twelfth piece of data from each end. The median is between the two middle values. In this case, because the two middle values are both 2, the median value is 2 cavities.

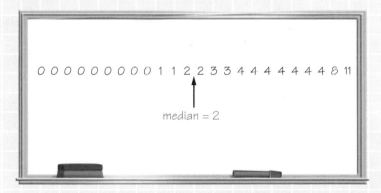

The middle of the range is 5.5 (halfway between 0 and 11), but the median number of cavities is 2. Knowing that the data range from 0 to 11 and that the median is 2 tells us that there are as many children in the group with 0 to 2 cavities as there are children with 2 to 11 cavities. At least half the children had 2 or fewer cavities.

If the two middle values are not the same, as in the data sets below, the median is midway between the two values, even if that value is not itself the value of any piece of data in the set.

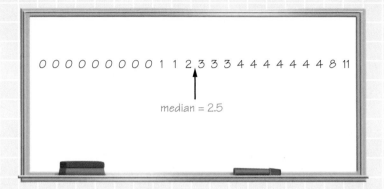

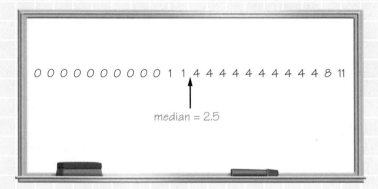

The median is introduced to fourth graders as one statistical measure that is useful in summarizing data. However, in years of field experience and work with teachers, we have found that understanding how to find the median and, more importantly, understanding what the median does and does not tell you about the data is quite complex. Like calculating the mean, which students study in middle school, learning to find this measure can be learned at this age, but understanding its use as a meaningful statistic is complex. What is most important is that students learn to describe the shape of the data: where the data are concentrated or clumped, where the data are spread out, and whether there are unusual values (outliers) in the data set. The median is one statistic that is helpful in describing and comparing data sets because it provides the information that *half the data are equal to or greater than that value,* and *half the data are equal to or less than that value.*

# Assessment: Comparing Numbers of Cavities

## Problems: 1 and 2

Benchmarks addressed:

**Benchmark 3:** Describe the shape of the data from a numerical data set, including where the data are concentrated and the highest, lowest, and median values.

**Benchmark 4:** Use data to compare two groups.

> **1a.** Make a line plot of the data about the number of cavities students have using the cavity data that your teacher distributes.
>
> **1b.** What do these data tell you about the number of cavities students in your class have?
>
> Consider the highest and lowest number of cavities and the outliers. Consider also where the data are concentrated and what you think is typical.

▲ Resource Masters, M7

**In order to meet the benchmarks, students' work should show that they can:**

- Make an accurate line plot of the cavity data from their own class or the data from Cavity Data from a Fourth Grade Class (M9);

- Describe what the data tells about the number of cavities students in the class have, using important aspects of the data in their description such as where the data are concentrated, the highest and lowest values, the median, and any outliers;

- Compare the two groups, referring to important aspects of the data.

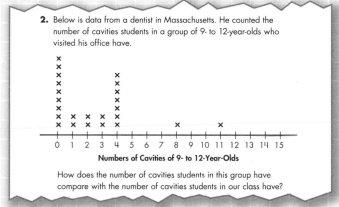

> **2.** Below is data from a dentist in Massachusetts. He counted the number of cavities students in a group of 9- to 12-year-olds who visited his office have.
>
> **Numbers of Cavities of 9- to 12-Year-Olds**
>
> How does the number of cavities students in this group have compare with the number of cavities students in our class have?

▲ Resource Masters, M8

It is expected that students at this point can make a line plot of a set of data. If students are not able to make an accurate line plot, they will need more practice during the rest of the unit with direct guidance from you or help from partners. The descriptions below focus on the two benchmarks—describing and comparing the data. Although students have been working on data for only five class sessions, many of these ideas were introduced in Grade 3 and should be familiar to students. This assessment will give you information early in the unit about which students are comfortable organizing and describing data and which students may need more support during Investigation 2.

## Meeting the Benchmarks

Students who meet the benchmarks describe what the data show about the numbers of cavities students in the class have, refer to important aspects of the data in their description, and then use this description to compare groups.

Students' descriptions may vary but should capture an overall sense of the shape of the data. Students should be able to tell a story about this group, using the data. Their description may include where the data are concentrated (where there are clumps), the amount of cavities more people have (the mode), where there is little data (number of cavities that few people have), the range from the highest value to the lowest value, or the median. They should refer to these aspects of the data as they compare groups.

> (1b) The range of our data is 0-7. the cluster of the data is between 0-2. The smallest part of the data is between 4-7.
>
> (2) Our model is the same as theres. What's different about ours and theres is our range was 0-7 and theirs is 0-11. The cluster for ours is between 0-2 and theres is 0-4.

*Derek's Work*

> (1b) its very clustered between 0-2. There's a small cluster between 6-7 Also 4's not in a cluster The mode is 0. the median is between 1 and 2. The range is 0-7. There is no outlier
>
> (a) the mode is the same as ours 2paople in both classes have 7cavities their range is 0-11 and ours is 0-7. They have a outlier, but we don't. Our median is 1.5 and their median is 2

*Anna's Work*

Both Anna and Derek accurately describe and compare the data, but it would be important for the teacher to check that they know what the numbers stand for. Only Anna mentions the word *cavity* once in her description. As the unit progresses, the teacher can help these students make sure that they make clear what the numbers represent;

e.g., instead of writing "The cluster of the data is between 0–2. The smallest part of the data is between 4–7," Derek could say, "Most students have between 0 and 2 cavities. Just a few have between 4 and 7." Certainly, students do not need to do this in every sentence, but they can learn to choose as Andrew does where it is most important to mention what the numbers represent.

> what I notice was that the median is 1 almost half of the class don't have cavities I also notice that there is a really short range

*Andrew's Work*

By the End-of-Unit Assessment, students should be clearly relating the data to the context, not writing statements that include only numbers.

## Partially Meeting the Benchmarks

Students who partially meet the benchmarks can make a line plot of the data and correctly "read" individual facts from the representation. However, they have difficulty seeing the data as a whole and comparing groups. What characterizes these students' work is that each statement is a separate statement of fact and they do not notice where the data are concentrated, except to say that a certain number of data points are at a certain value. In general, they also simply have fewer observations about the data.

For example, for Problem 1a, Sabrina wrote:

> I noticed that more people don't have any cavities. I also know that only one person has 7.

*Sabrina's Work*

In comparing the two groups, Helena wrote:

> I notice that both of the data the mode is 0. And in both classes two people have 1 cavity. Nobody has 5 cavities on 2 both graphs.

*Helena's Work*

Students who partially meet the benchmark will benefit from continuing to have opportunities to describe data verbally and in writing in the next two investigations. As they continue to describe data, help them expand their descriptions to include both important aspects of the data and what the data tell about the group. Help them move toward describing more of the overall shape of the data by asking questions such as these:

- You gave important information about these data. You said that more people don't have any cavities. Do you know what that is called?

- What else can you say about the data?

- Many people have no cavities. Is there a clump of data near 0?

- You told me how many people have 0 cavities and how many people have 7 cavities. What about the people in between? Are they closer to 0 or closer to 7?

- What does that tell us about the number of cavities of people in this class?

## Not Meeting the Benchmarks

Students who do not meet the benchmarks may not be able to gather information from representations of the data. In many cases this may mean that they are unable to interpret the data representation. They may be able to say that there are 5 Xs on 2, but they may not know what those Xs stand for. They may not be sure whether, for example, the numbers on the line plot stand for the numbers of cavities or the numbers of people. Their descriptions may be vague and not tied to the context of the data.

Students who do not meet the benchmarks need more practice reading representations and reporting the information given in a line plot. Collecting data in contexts with which they are familiar and making predictions about what their data will show can also help students bring meaning to the data. They will have a chance to do this as they design and carry out their own survey in Investigation 2.

# Teacher Note

# Numerical and Categorical Data

In Investigations 1 and 2, students work with *numerical data*—numbers that represent quantities that can be ordered. In statistics, there are different kinds of numerical data, or quantitative data, that behave in different ways. In this unit, students work with two kinds of numerical data: 1) data that result from counting something (such as the number of raisins in a box or the number of cavities a person has) and 2) data that result from measuring something (such as their heights and the heights of first graders).

Because numerical data represent a quantity of something, they can be represented along a scale as in a line plot.

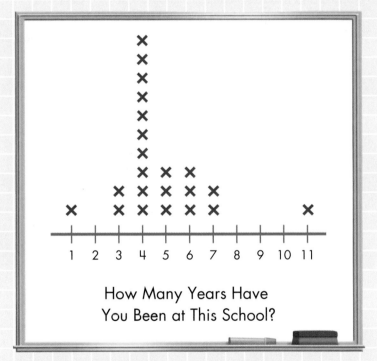

How Many Years Have
You Been at This School?

By looking at the data in order, we can see the range of the data and how the data are distributed across that range—where they are concentrated, where they are spread out, where there are gaps in the data, and whether there is an outlier. On the line plot, we can see the shape of the data. See **Teacher Note:** Focusing on the Shape of the Data, page 123, and **Teacher Note:** Data Terms and

Representations, page 121, for more about describing numerical data and for definitions of important statistical terms.

This way of describing data is something that we cannot do with categorical data. Categorical data have values that can be classified in categories but cannot be ordered by numerical value. An example of a question that results in categorical data is, "What color eyes do you have?" The data collected to answer this question in your class would have values such as *blue, brown, black, hazel,* or *gray.* The values of the data can be classified and graphed, but they do not have an inherent order: blue is not *more* or *less* than brown or black. Categorical data are not quantities, so we cannot put them in order. They don't have a range or outliers. Most statistical measures, such as the *median,* which students encounter in Investigation 1, can be applied only to numerical data. However, categorical data can have a *mode.* For example, *brown* might be the mode in a survey of eye color.

Fourth graders do not need to use the terms *categorical* and *numerical.* However, when they choose their survey question in Investigation 2, they do need to understand that they are coming up with a question that will result in data that are quantities.

Sometimes students come up with a data question that does result in a number, but the number does not represent a quantity of something. In some classes, questions such as "What is your favorite number?" came up. This question does result in a number as an answer, but that number does not represent a quantity of something. Data collected with this question are actually categorical data. This distinction can be a difficult one for fourth graders. One way to explain this to your students is that when they ask their question, the answer should be *an amount of something.* They need to come up with a question for which each person they ask will count or measure something in order to answer them.

# Teacher Note

# Collecting Data from Other Classes

Teachers have developed many approaches to the complicated process of collecting data from other classrooms. Ideally, students undertake this process themselves. They are more invested in the data and learn more about the process of defining data questions and carrying out a data investigation when they are directly involved. However, many factors may make it difficult for you to send students to other classrooms to collect data, including your and other teachers' schedules, the size of the school, and the familiarity of your students with the school. Here are approaches teachers have used in a variety of schools for collecting data from other classrooms. They are listed in order from most student direct involvement to least student direct involvement.

1. Students visit other classrooms, interview each student, and record their responses. (If teachers can provide a class list, the list will help your students keep track of which students they have asked.)

2. Students bring their questions and a stack of index cards (or stick-on notes or scrap paper) to another class. The students read the questions to the class, and each student in the other class records his or her response. This can be a more efficient procedure that will interrupt the other class for only a few minutes. In addition, students can respond anonymously, which may be more comfortable for some students. However, this approach may work only in grades in which students are old enough to write.

3. Students bring their questions to the teacher, who collects the data from her students at a convenient time and then returns the data to you. Students will need to print their questions clearly at the top of a piece of lined paper along with any explanation of their question that they think will help make them clear to other students.

4. Students give you their questions (written clearly, as explained in Suggestion 3). You drop them off with other teachers, who then collect and return the data to you.

# About the Mystery Data

**To the teacher: STOP! Don't look!**

**Before you read the following descriptions of the Mystery Data sets on *Student Activity Book* pages 25–27 and ruin the surprise, don't you want to try solving the mysteries yourself?**

The Mystery Data pages each contain measurements of individuals in some real group of living things. The living things in each set are closely related in some way. Each group is something about which data may logically be collected—not some random assortment of disparate things.

Here are the actual data, which may be guessed by students or revealed by you during the discussion in Session 2.6.

*Mystery Data A (Student Activity Book page 25)*

These values are the heights of the basketball players who were selected to play in the 2004 NBA All-Star Game on February 15, 2004, in Los Angeles, California. The West team won, 136–132.

| West Team | Height | Position, Team |
|-----------|--------|----------------|
| Tim Duncan | 84″ (7′0″) | forward, San Antonio Spurs |
| Kevin Garnett | 83″ (6′11″) | forward, Minnesota Timberwolves |
| Kobe Bryant | 78″ (6′6″) | guard, Los Angeles Lakers |
| Steve Francis | 75″ (6′3″) | guard, Houston Rockets |
| Yao Ming | 90″ (7′6″) | center, Houston Rockets |
| Ray Allen | 77″ (6′5″) | guard, Seattle SuperSonics |
| Sam Cassell | 75″ (6′3″) | guard, Minnesota Timberwolves |
| Andrei Kirilenko | 81″ (6′9″) | forward, Utah Jazz |
| Brad Miller | 84″ (7′0″) | center, Sacramento Kings |
| Dirk Nowitzki | 84″ (7′0″) | forward, Dallas Mavericks |
| Shaquille O'Neal | 85″ (7′1″) | center, Los Angeles Lakers |
| Peja Stojakovic | 82″ (6′10″) | guard, Sacramento Kings |

| East Team | Height | Position, Team |
|-----------|--------|----------------|
| Vince Carter | 78″ (6′6″) | forward, Toronto Raptors |
| Jermaine O'Neal | 83″ (6′11″) | forward, Indiana Pacers |
| Allen Iverson | 72″ (6′0″) | guard, Philadelphia 76ers |
| Tracy McGrady | 80″ (6′8″) | guard, Orlando Magic |
| Ben Wallace | 81″ (6′9″) | center, Detroit Pistons |
| Ron Artest | 79″ (6′7″) | forward, Indiana Pacers |
| Baron Davis | 75″ (6′3″) | guard, New Orleans Hornets |
| Jason Kidd | 76″ (6′4″) | guard, New Jersey Nets |
| Jamaal Magloire | 83″ (6′11″) | center, New Orleans Hornets |
| Kenyon Martin | 81″ (6′9″) | forward, New Jersey Nets |
| Paul Pierce | 78″ (6′6″) | forward, Boston Celtics |
| Michael Redd | 78″ (6′6″) | guard, Milwaukee Bucks |

(Source: *http://www.nba.com/allstar2004/allstar_game/index.html*)

Mystery Data B (*Student Activity Book* page 26)

These values are the lengths of 18 boa constrictors living in various museums or zoos in the United States.

| Name | Length | Location |
|------|--------|----------|
| Shannon | 116″ (9′8″) | Boston Museum of Science |
| Tony | 86″ (7′2″) | Boston Museum of Science |
| Bambi | 94″ (7′10″) | Boston Museum of Science |
| Bob | 54″ (4′6″) | Boston Museum of Science |
| Tiger | 79″ (6′7″) | Boston Museum of Science |
| Saulette | 108″ (9′0″) | Franklin Park Children's Zoo |
| Jake | 114″ (9′6″) | Franklin Park Children's Zoo |
| Bella | 84″ (7′0″) | Worcester Science Center |
| Floyd | 72″ (6′0″) | Worcester Science Center |
| Boa | 54″ (4′6″) | Worcester Science Center |
| Lady | 96″ (8′0″) | Earlham College |
| Sleeper | 72″ (6′0″) | Boston University |
| Malcolm | 80″ (6′8″) | Science Museum of Connecticut |
| Godzilla | 93″ (7′9″) | Science Museum of Connecticut |
| Alexis | 72″ (6′0″) | Science Museum of Connecticut |
| Julius | 64″ (5′4″) | Science Museum of Connecticut |
| unnamed | 63″ (5′3″) | Busch Gardens |
| unnamed | 78″ (6′6″) | Busch Gardens |

(Source: Boston Museum of Science; Franklin Park Children's Zoo, Boston; Worcester Science Center, Worcester, MA; Earlham College, Richmond, IN; Boston University; Science Museum of Connecticut, Hartford, CT; and Busch Gardens, Tampa, FL. Lengths given by the Worcester Science Center and Boston University are estimates. Data collected in 1989.)

Mystery Data C (*Student Activity Book* page 27)

These values are the lengths at birth of a group of 30 babies born at Brigham and Women's Hospital, Boston, Massachusetts, from March 10 to March 16, 2005.

| | | | | | | |
|------|------|------|------|------|------|------|
| 18.5″ | 19.5″ | 19″ | 20″ | 19″ | 20″ | 20″ |
| 18.5″ | 18″ | 21.5″ | 22″ | 19″ | 19″ | 19.5″ |
| 19″ | 18″ | 20″ | 20″ | 21″ | 20″ | 20″ |
| 20″ | 19″ | 19″ | 20.5″ | 19″ | 19″ | 19.5″ |
| 19″ | 20″ | | | | | |

(Source: *http://www.brighamandwomens.org/patient/webnursery.asp;* data gathered Fall, 2005)

# Teacher Note

# Impossible, Certain, and Everything in Between

The first concept students meet in this unit is that probability describes different levels of possibility. By considering a variety of future events, they discover that some events are impossible, some definitely occur, and most are somewhere in between. By mathematical convention, 0 is assigned as the probability for an event that will never occur and 1 as the probability for an event that will definitely occur. Events in between are given probability values that are fractions between 0 and 1.

For some of the events your students discuss in these beginning sessions, the assigned probability is a matter of opinion until data are collected that allow an estimate. For example, weather predictions are based on data. For other events, students can determine the probability theoretically. For example, rolling a 6 on a number cube that has the numbers 1 through 6 on its faces has a theoretical probability of $\frac{1}{6}$, or 1 out of 6 chances. In both cases, probabilities are expressed as fractions, decimals, or percents.

To understand what these fractions mean, consider the point halfway between 0 and 1. In terms of probability, we label this point $\frac{1}{2}$ or 0.5. We can say, for example, "There is a $\frac{1}{2}$ chance of getting a head when you flip a coin," or "The event has a probability of 0.5." These phrases indicate that heads and tails are equally likely; they have the same probability of occurring. The probability of rolling an odd number on a number cube is $\frac{3}{6}$ or $\frac{1}{2}$ because, of the six equally likely events, three of them (1, 3, 5) are odd numbers.

You can sometimes interpret the fraction $\frac{1}{2}$ as "1 out of 2," meaning that of the two equally likely ways the coin can land, one of them will result in heads. In the context of probability, reading a fraction in this way is often easier for students to understand than using the term *one half.* Although "1 out of 2" may seem a more natural way for young students to express the probability $\frac{1}{2}$, the phrase can be misleading. It is not always true that an event with a probability of $\frac{1}{2}$ is one of two events. For example, if a bag contains 10 red cubes, 5 blue cubes, and 5 yellow cubes, the probability of pulling out a red cube is $\frac{1}{2}$, but there are three possible outcomes (red, blue, and yellow), so "1 out of 2" does not refer here to 1 out of 2 possible outcomes but to the probability of each chosen cube's being red.

This way of talking about probability is referred to as *theoretical* probability because it describes what would happen *in theory* when we consider events that have a certain number of possible outcomes. However, probability in our lives does not work exactly as it does *in theory*. If we actually roll a number cube 10 times, we may get an odd number exactly half of the time (5 times), but we may get an odd number only 4 times out of 10 or 6 times out of 10. This way of talking about probability is referred to as *experimental* probability because it describes what happens when we do an experiment such as rolling a number cube 10 times.

Perhaps the most important concept of this investigation is understanding the difference between theoretical and experimental probability. Although students do not use these terms, they carry out probability experiments in which they can see that their results are usually not exactly what they expect according to theoretical probability and that they seldom get identical results when they repeat an experiment.

Students' intuitions and our own intuitions, based on our experiences, indicate that theoretical and experimental probability are not the same. If a coin is tossed 10 times, we are not surprised if it comes up heads 6 or even 7 times. But 10 heads out of 10 makes us suspicious. If a coin repeatedly lands more often on heads, we begin to suspect that the coin is not fair.

Here's how these intuitions fit into the mathematical concept of probability. When we actually flip a coin 10 times, we may well get 4 heads, 6 heads or even occasionally 8 heads out of 10. If we repeated a series of 10 flips 100 times, we could keep track of how many times we got each possible result. We are likely (but not guaranteed) to get 5 heads out of 10 more frequently than any other result—with 4 or 6 heads next most likely, 3 or 7 next most likely, and so on. This graph shows the results we got when we repeated a series of 10 flips of a coin 100 times:

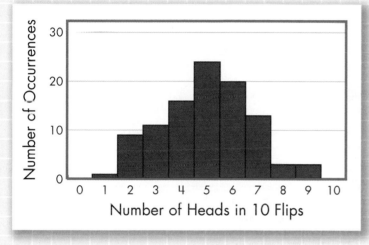

The most important things to notice about this graph are the following:

- Five heads is one of the most frequent results (24 of the 100 trials resulted in 5 heads).

- The distribution is centered around 5 (the median is exactly 5; the mean is 4.98).

- The distribution is roughly symmetrical around the center value of 5.

- The distribution is generally mound-shaped. The farther from 5 heads out of 10, the fewer occurrences there are. We got 1 head once, 9 heads twice, and never 0 or 10 heads. These extreme results are very unlikely and thus surprise us when they happen—although they *are* possible.

If probability does not tell us precisely what will happen, what does it tell us? We cannot predict for a given set of coin flips exactly what we will get, but we do know something about a large collection of sets of 10 flips. Furthermore, if we continue to flip a fair coin a large number of times, the occurrence of heads will get closer and closer to $\frac{1}{2}$ or 50 percent. This is one way that probability theory connects a theoretical probability of $\frac{1}{2}$ with what actually happens when a coin is tossed.

# Teacher Note

# End-of-Unit Assessment

## Problem 1

Benchmark addressed:

**Benchmark 6:** Describe the likelihood of an event in terms of a scale from impossible (probability of 0) to certain (probability of 1).

**In order to meet the benchmark, students' work should show that they can:**

- Place the events correctly on the Likelihood Line;

- Give reasonable explanations for where they placed Events A and C, based on the probability of the events.

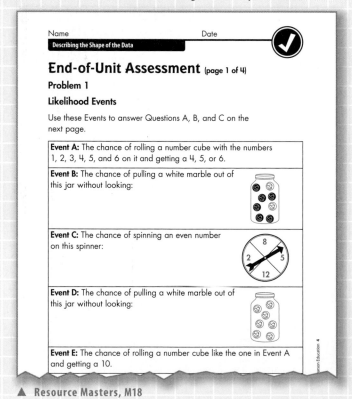

▲ **Resource Masters, M18**

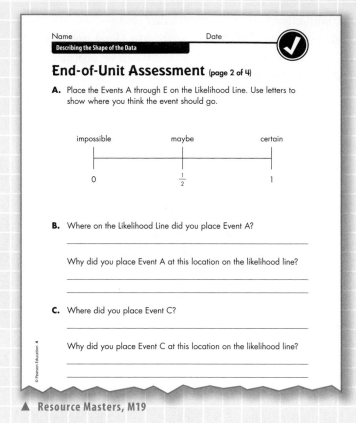

▲ **Resource Masters, M19**

## Meeting the Benchmark

Students who meet the benchmark place at least four of the five events correctly on the Likelihood Line and give reasonable explanations for where they placed Events A and C. The correct placement of the five events is shown below.

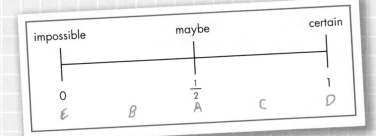

*Enrique's Work*

Students' explanation of placing Event A, rolling either a 4, 5, or 6 on a number cube, should include the idea that 4, 5, and 6 are half of the numbers on the number cube, so that there is a 3 out of 6, or 1 out of 2, probability of rolling one of those three numbers. Similarly, explanations for the placement of Event C should include the idea that three out of the four numbers on the spinner are even, or at least that there are more even numbers than odd numbers. Students may state the probability exactly as $\frac{3}{4}$ or 75 percent, or they can say that it is between $\frac{1}{2}$ and 1.

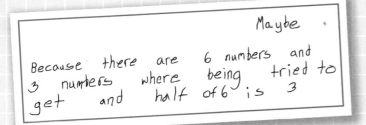

*Maybe*

Because there are 6 numbers and 3 numbers where being tried to get and half of 6 is 3

*Enrique's Work*

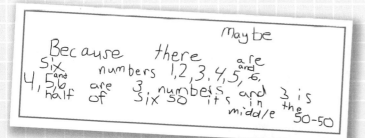

*Maybe*

Because there are six numbers 1,2,3,4,5,6, and 4,5,6 are 3, numbers and 3 is half of six so it's in the middle the 50-50

*Emaan's Work*

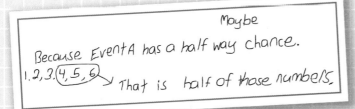

*Maybe*

Because Event A has a half way chance.
1,2,3,(4,5,6) That is half of those numbers.

*Cheyenne's Work*

## Partially Meeting and Not Meeting the Benchmark

Some students who partially meet the benchmark are able to correctly place the events on the Likelihood Line but are not able to give a reasonable explanation for where they placed the events. Others place at least three events correctly on the Likelihood Line, but they are not able to place the other two events and have at least one weak explanation for how they placed Events A and C. Students who do not meet the benchmark place fewer than three events correctly and have inadequate explanations for placing the events. The explanation is unclear, is based on personal opinion, or does not match the placement of the event.

The placement of Event A or C is correct, but the explanation, although it may hint at some elements of understanding, does not relate the chance of that event to the total number of possible events (e.g., 3 out of 4 chances) or to the number of other possible events (3 chances of even, only one chance of odd).

Because it's a very close chance and it would be very good if you rolled a 4,5 or a six.

*Sabrina's Work*

I put Event A at this location because there's chance not even getting a five, a four or even a six and there is a chance to get one of those numbers.

*Ramona's Work*

'cause its most likely to happen

*Derek's Work*

To get a better idea of what students in the examples above are understanding or not understanding, ask them about their explanations. Some students may have difficulty putting into words what they understand about the probability of these events. This is less an issue of understanding probability concepts and more an issue of expressing that understanding. These students will need some support in how to clearly explain the probability of events.

> Because there is a chance of getting an even number because their are 3 even numben

*Bill's Work*

> because 12 is an even number

*Damian's Work*

> because it is a good place for it

*Alejandro's Work*

Students who do not meet the benchmark can use more experience describing the probability of events in words (impossible, unlikely, maybe, and so on) and relating those events to the benchmarks of 0, $\frac{1}{2}$, and 1.

**Note:** Students may misunderstand part of the problem. For example, they are not sure what an even number is or don't understand certain fractional values.

> because there are two even #s and 2 odd #s

*Terrell's Work*

> I placed Event A in its location because Event A's answer was 3/6 and I estimated where that would be.

*LaTanya's Work*

In these cases, you may want to speak to the students about the problems. Their misunderstandings may have nothing to do with the benchmarks for this unit but with other parts of the context of the problem. It is important for you to sort out which mathematical ideas they do understand and which are causing confusion. Sometimes this kind of response indicates a careless error: "Oh, I looked at that fast and I was thinking 21 instead of 12, so I thought there were only two even numbers." In such cases, ask students to revise their responses so that you can get an accurate assessment of the benchmarks for this unit.

# Problem 2

**Benchmark addressed:**

**Benchmark 3:** Describe the shape of the data from a numerical data set including where the data are concentrated and the highest, lowest, and median values.

**In order to meet the benchmark, students' work should show that they can:**

- Describe accurately what the data show about the temperatures in Philadelphia in July 2003;

- Refer accurately to important aspects of the data in their description, such as where the data are concentrated, the highest and lowest values, the median, and outliers.

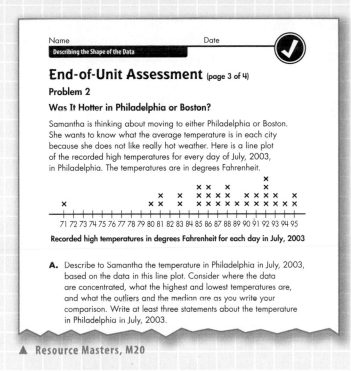

**Name** _____ **Date** _____

Describing the Shape of the Data

## End-of-Unit Assessment (page 3 of 4)

**Problem 2**

**Was It Hotter in Philadelphia or Boston?**

Samantha is thinking about moving to either Philadelphia or Boston. She wants to know what the average temperature is in each city because she does not like really hot weather. Here is a line plot of the recorded high temperatures for every day of July, 2003, in Philadelphia. The temperatures are in degrees Fahrenheit.

71 72 73 74 75 76 77 78 79 80 81 82 83 84 85 86 87 88 89 90 91 92 93 94 95

Recorded high temperatures in degrees Fahrenheit for each day in July, 2003

**A.** Describe to Samantha the temperature in Philadelphia in July, 2003, based on the data in this line plot. Consider where the data are concentrated, what the highest and lowest temperatures are, and what the outliers and the median are as you write your comparison. Write at least three statements about the temperature in Philadelphia in July, 2003.

▲ Resource Masters, M20

## Meeting the Benchmark

Students who meet the benchmark describe what the data show about temperature in Philadelphia and refer to important aspects of the data. Their responses will vary in how they describe the data, but it is important that, by this time in the unit, they make it clear that the numbers refer to temperatures and that they make at least one statement about the overall shape of the data. In this data set, they should notice that most of the temperatures are in the high 80s and low 90s, and they should comment on other aspects of the data such as the range, the median, and/or the outlier. Here are two examples.

> It's pretty hot out but not really hot the usuall temp is between 85° and 95°, but your more likely to have it in the 80's. The coolist temperture was 71° and hottest was 95°. 71 was a outlier.

*Abdul's Work*

> The temperature in July 2003 in Philadelphia is from 85 to 95 degrees most of the time.
>
> The median temperature in Philadelphia is 88°F
>
> The outliar is 71°F.
>
> There is a clump from 85°F to 95°F.

*Marisol's Work*

Kimberly's work could be improved by identifying a central clump of data, but her description is still good enough to meet the benchmark.

> 1. In philidelphia the temperatures are in the 80-90 Range.
> 2. 71 is an outlier, so don't expect to much of that weather
> 3. It was 92 most, so it is pretty hot!

*Kimberly's Work*

## Partially Meeting the Benchmark

Students who partially meet the benchmark may describe important aspects of the graph but not describe what these numbers indicate about the temperature in Philadelphia in July, 2003.

> 1. From 85 to 95 its clumped and has 25.
> 2. The range is 71 to 95
> 3. 71 is a outlier

*Benson's Work*

> One statement is there is a clump from 85-95. Second an outlier is 71 there are 8 numbers between it and the next number with data on it. Third the range is 71-95.

*Anna's Work*

Students will continue to have opportunities to describe data in other units this year during the Ten-Minute Math activity, *Quick Surveys,* which was introduced in this unit. When these students describe data, encourage them both to describe the data and to be clear about what the data tell them about what the data represent. Use questions such as this:

**You said that there was a big cluster between 85 and 95. What does that tell you about the temperature in Philadelphia in July, 2003?**

Note that some students misinterpreted this graph as though it were showing temperature change over time. Students worked with line graphs showing temperature over time in Grade 3. For example, Steve writes:

> Samantha First it was pretty cold and hot a mixture. Number two there's a huge gap between 71 and 80 so it grew hot over days and there's a huge clump between 85 and 88. Third the hottest it's been was only 95 degrees Fahrenheit in Philadolphia.

*Steve's Work*

Although Steve does misinterpret the graph as though it were showing the order in which these temperatures occurred, he nevertheless describes some important features of the data, in particular the lump from 85–88 degrees.

One might also wonder whether Steve has experience with temperature benchmarks because he says that it was "only 95 degrees," as though that were not very hot.

## Not Meeting the Benchmark

Students who do not meet the benchmark are not able to describe the overall shape and important features of the data. For example, Lucy mentions only the mode.

> There are a lot of 92 and it was hot that year it looks like a canyon

*Lucy's Work*

Her statement, "It looks like a canyon," seems to refer to a shape she sees on the graph, as though the graph were only a picture rather than a representation of data.

Ask students who do not meet the benchmark about their descriptions to learn more about their understanding of describing data. In talking to the students, it will be easier to determine whether they are having difficulty explaining what they notice about the data or whether they do not understand how to read the graph and describe the data.

Some students who do not meet the benchmark may be having difficulty reading and interpreting a representation. For example, they may not understand the meaning of the Xs and the numbers on the graph. These students need more opportunities to read and interpret representations. Keep these students in mind during the Ten-Minute Math activity *Quick Survey,* and choose contexts for data collection that you know have meaning for them. It is important that they work with representations of data to which they can bring familiarity and experience. Besides reading and describing data representations during this activity, these students can benefit from brief follow-up conversations with you, in which you look together at the representation of the data and talk with them about what they notice about the data collected by the class.

# Problem 2: Parts B, C, and D

**Benchmarks addressed:**

**Benchmark 4:** Use data to compare two groups.

**Benchmark 5:** Use evidence from a set of data to support an argument.

**In order to meet the benchmarks, students' work should show that they can:**

- Accurately create a line plot of the temperature data for Boston in July, 2003;

- Compare important aspects of the temperature data for Boston with important aspects of the temperature data for Philadelphia;

- Explain what the data show about how the temperatures in the two cities compare;

- Give evidence from the data to support their argument about which city was hotter in July.

---

**B.** Make a line plot of the temperatures in Boston in July, 2003, on a separate piece of paper.

**C.** What can you tell Samantha about how the temperature in Boston in July compared with the temperature in Philadelphia? Write at least three statements that compare the temperatures in the two cities in July. Consider where the data are concentrated, what the highest and lowest temperatures are, any outliers, and what the medians are as you write your comparison.

_____
_____
_____
_____

**D.** According to these data, would you tell Samantha that July, 2003, was a hotter month in Boston or in Philadelphia? Use the data to support your answer.

▲ **Resource Masters, M21**

---

## Meeting the Benchmarks

Students who meet the benchmarks compare aspects of the data and connect the data to what it shows about how the temperatures in the two cities compare. They give evidence from the data to support whether they thought it was hotter in July in Philadelphia or Boston. Their responses will differ in how they compare the data and what evidence they use to support their arguments.

Ursula starts out by comparing the lowest temperatures, the highest temperatures, where the data is concentrated, and the medians.

In Boston the lowest tempeture is lower than the lowest tempeture in Phily also the highest tempeture in Boston is lower then the highest temp in Phily The temp in Boston is usually around 80-86 but in Phily it is 85-95 so it seems to be hotter in Phily. The average temp in Phily is 88 and in boston its 82 hotter in Phily.

*Ursula's Work*

Nadeem begins with a good estimate of how the overall temperatures compare and also describes how spread out the data are.

In philadelphia the tempature is hotter that boston by about 5/10° In boston the tempatures are more spread out in philadelphia they are more clumped together Philadelphia stays more at one tempature Boston is more spread out.

*Nadeem's Work*

It may be that Nadeem used the median or looked at how the Philadelphia data are shifted to the right in comparison with the Boston data.

When supporting their argument about which city had hotter temperatures in July, students might refer to where the data are concentrated or to the median temperatures. In some way, they should describe that the Philadelphia temperatures overall are concentrated in higher values than the Boston data. Their arguments should not be limited to comparing only the highest and lowest temperatures.

Philadelphia is hotter because in Philadelphia they have 13 days 90° or above. In Boston they have 3 in 90° or above. Also the high in Philadelphia is 95 and in Boston is 93.

*Kimberly's Work*

July is a hotter month in Philadelphia. the main temperatures are 85-95 and in Boston it is 80 -86.

*Terrell's Work*

## Partially Meeting the Benchmarks

Students who partially meet the benchmarks may make a strong comparison but incorrectly describe some aspects of the data. For example, Tonya incorrectly calculates the median. Tonya appears to have found the midpoint of the range rather than the middle value in the data. She does not seem to notice that, for example, most of the Philadelphia data is above 83 degrees, so 83 degrees is not a good representative value.

① 66 is it cooist, then 72 and 73. In Philodphia the coolist was 76
② The hotist in Philadelphia was 90. the hotist in Boston was 93.
③ The median number in Philadelphia was 83, is was 83% twice. The median number in Boston is 80, it was 80% once.
④ The bigest coump of temp in Philaelphia was 89-95. The biggest in Boston was 80-83.

*Tonya's Work*

Other students who partially meet the benchmarks make accurate statements about the data but do not use the data to make an argument about which city was hotter.

The outlier in Philadelphia is 71°F and the outliers in Boston is 66.

The median is 88°F in Philadelphia and in Boston it is 82°F.

In Boston the clump is from 80 to 86 and in Phildlo it is 85 to 95.

*Bill's Work*

Talking with students who partially meet the benchmarks will give you more information about what they understand and don't understand about comparing data and using evidence from data to support an argument.

All students who partially meet the benchmarks can benefit from more opportunities to compare data and support an argument with evidence from a set of data. As part of the *Quick Survey* Ten-Minute Math activity, you may want to include some opportunities to compare two sets of data. Some students may simply need to be encouraged to write fuller responses. Others may need help making the connections between the aspects of the data they are able to describe and what those aspects tell them about what the data represent.

## Not Meeting the Benchmarks

Students who do not meet the benchmarks may compare only the highest and lowest temperatures, describe the data only in terms of numbers without relating those numbers to temperatures, or simply assert that one city is hotter without using the data to support their argument.

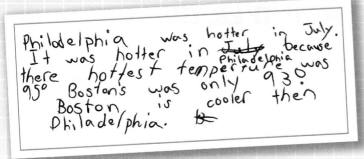

*Marisol's Work*

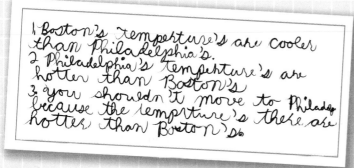

*Yuson's Work*

Students who are not giving evidence from the data for their comparisons need to be encouraged to explain what in the data shows their conclusions.

As in Problem 1, some students who do not meet the benchmark may be having difficulty reading and interpreting a representation. For example, they may not realize what the Xs and the numbers mean. These students need more opportunities to read and interpret representations.

Students who do not meet the benchmarks need more opportunities to compare data and use evidence from data to support an argument. As part of the *Quick Survey* Ten-Minute Math activity, you may want to include some opportunities to compare two sets of data. Students who are comparing only highest and lowest values need support in looking at other aspects of the data. As they compare data, you might ask them questions such as this:

- What else do you notice about the data in between the highest and lowest temperatures? How are those data similar or different?

# Describing the Shape of the Raisin Data

This fourth-grade class is examining a line plot for the first time in this unit. They are describing what the line plot tells them about how many raisins are in a box. As the students talk, the teacher encourages them to describe the overall shape of the data.

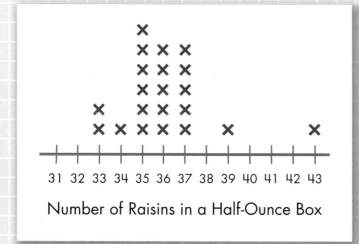

Number of Raisins in a Half-Ounce Box

**Teacher:** So what can you say about the raisin data? Let's hear a few of your ideas.

**Jill:** There are a lot at 35.

**Derek:** There was only one at 39 and one at 43.

**Marisol:** There are two at 33 and one at 34.

**Lucy:** And 33 is the lowest.

**Teacher:** So no boxes had fewer than 33 raisins?

**Derek:** Yeah. And 43 was the highest.

**Teacher:** So the amount of raisins in a box ranged from 33 to 43. What else?

**Jake:** There's nothing at 38, 40, 41, or 42.

**Teacher:** Jake's noticing that there are some holes in this part of the data. Can anyone say any more about that?

**Yuson:** There's nothing at 31 or 32 either.

**Teacher:** Thirty-three is the lowest count and there's nothing below it. But the situation that Jake noticed up here is a little different. What can you say about that?

**Terrell:** Mostly, the raisins go from 33 to 37, but sometimes you get something higher.

**Teacher:** Can anyone add to that?

**Steve:** You'd be really lucky if you were the one who got 43!

**Teacher:** Mathematicians have a name for a piece of data that is far away from all the rest. They call it an *outlier*. An outlier is an unusual piece of data—sometimes it's an error, but sometimes it's just an unusual piece of data. It's often interesting to try to find out more about an outlier. Who had this outlier?

**Enrique:** I did. And I counted twice, and Luke checked it, too, so I know it was 43.

**Marisol:** Maybe he's got smaller raisins.

**Teacher:** So if someone asked you, "What's the typical number of raisins in a box?" what would you say? What number of raisins would you typically expect?

**Ursula:** I'd say 35.

The teacher addresses the class as a whole.

**Teacher:** Why would 35 be a reasonable description of how many raisins are in a box?

**Tonya:** Because the most boxes had 35.

**Teacher:** So, you wouldn't be surprised to get 35 raisins in a box. Are there other amounts that would seem fairly typical or usual?

**Luke:** I wouldn't say just 35.

**Teacher:** Why not?

**Luke:** There's really not that much difference between 33, 34, 35, 36, 37. They're all really close together. I'd say 33 to 37 because the 39 and 43 aren't what you'd usually get.

**Teacher:** So Luke is saying that he'd use an interval to describe the raisins, from 33 to 37, and Tonya said that she'd say that 35 was typical. What do other people think about that?

In this discussion, the class has moved gradually from describing individual features of the data to looking at the shape of the data as a whole. The teacher introduces the term *outlier* because it came up naturally in the discussion and highlights important aspects of the data such as the highest and lowest values and where there are gaps in the data. Throughout, the teacher asks students to give reasons for their ideas and pushes them to think further by asking for additions or alternatives to ideas students raise. Students continue to consider these features of data and what information they provide as they work through this unit.

# What Is a Typical Height?

After describing their height data, this class considers a "typical" height for their class during the discussion Describing the Class Height Data, page 33, in Session 1.2.

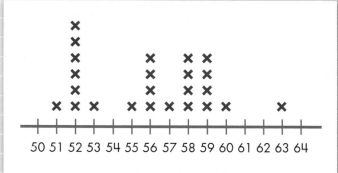

Heights of Fourth-Grade Students in Inches

**Teacher:** Suppose that someone asked you, "About how tall are fourth graders in your class?" What's a fairly typical height for our class?

**Damian:** We think you should pick a number that comes up the most, so we picked 52, because there are more 52s than any other number.

**Teacher:** What does everyone else think about that method?

**Cheyenne:** We did the same thing. There are a lot of 52s, so that seemed like what was typical.

**Teacher:** Did anybody make a different choice?

**Jill:** We came out with 58.

**Teacher:** So your choice is a little higher than what Damian's and Cheyenne's groups picked. Why do you think that's reasonable?

**Jill:** I don't know. It just seemed like that would be it.

**Teacher:** But I'm interested in your reason for 58.

**Jill:** There's a big clump of data crowded around 58.

**Teacher:** Yes, that's an interesting method. I can see your reasons for both of these methods. Does anyone have a good argument for choosing one over the other for the most typical value for our class?

**Jake:** Even though 52 has the most, there are still only six kids at 52, but there are 13 kids bunched around 58.

**Teacher:** Where are you finding your 13 students, Jake?

**Jake:** From 56 to 59. That's more than half the class.

**Marisol:** Yeah, I think 52 is too low, like with the raisins, the typical number in a box wasn't the smallest or the largest, but somewhere in the middle.

**Teacher:** So you think a middle value is more typical. What do you think about that argument, Damian and Cheyenne? What if we were reporting about fourth graders' heights? What would people expect to see in a fourth-grade class, according to our data?

**Cheyenne:** Yeah, maybe I'd agree about a higher number. You'd see a lot of kids in the high 50s like Jake is saying, but you could see some in the low 50s too.

**Teacher:** I think Cheyenne is saying something important about our data. There are a lot of you in that 56 to 59 inch clump, but there is also a smaller clump around 52 inches.

These students are considering how to describe their heights overall. By looking at the shape of the line plot, they can see where data are concentrated. By juxtaposing student ideas, the teacher helps students think about what each idea adds to the description of the data. Asking students to summarize the data by thinking about what is "typical" is one way to help students focus on overall shape of the data, rather than simply listing the number of occurrences at each value (6 students are 52 inches, 4 students are 56, 58, and 59 inches, and so on). Summarizing data in this way becomes even more useful when comparing two groups, as students will do in Session 1.4.

# Dialogue Box

# What Does the Median Tell You?

These students worked on how to find the median of a data set and are now discussing what information the median provides.

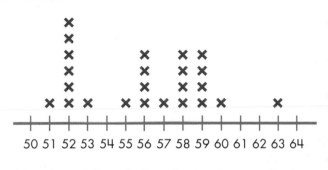

Heights of Fourth-Grade Students in Inches

**Teacher:** So you know how to find a median. But what good is knowing the median? Why do you think statisticians or other scientists are interested in knowing the median of a set of data?

**Bill:** It's the middle number.

**Teacher:** Yes, it is the middle number; for example, the middle height in our class is 56 inches. But if you knew that the median height of some other class was 56 inches, too, what would you know about that other class?

**Sabrina:** If they lined up, the middle kid would be 56 inches tall.

**Teacher:** Yes; what else?

**Emaan:** I don't agree with Sabrina, because it might not be the middle kid. It might be between the two kids in the middle.

**Teacher:** So you're both saying that 56 inches is the middle value either way. How does that help us know something about the height of the class?

**Kimberly:** You know that half the kids are below 56 and half the kids are taller.

**Yuki:** They're like our class, about the same height.

**Teacher:** They're like our class. What does that mean?

**Yuki:** The middle of their heights is 56 inches and so is ours.

**Teacher:** What else could you say about whether they're like us or not?

**LaTanya:** They wouldn't have to be exactly alike. They could have some kids who were much taller than kids in our class.

**Teacher:** How would that work?

**LaTanya:** The middle kid could still be 56 inches, but the kids taller than 56 inches could reach all the way up to 80 inches.

**Teacher:** So the top half could be more spread out. What do other people think?

**Sabrina:** I don't think it would be that spread out. Fourth graders aren't 80 inches tall.

The class takes a minute to estimate how tall 80 inches is and then resumes the discussion.

**Teacher:** So you're saying that you have some experience that tells you that another fourth grade class with a median height of 56 inches wouldn't be as drastically different from ours as LaTanya was saying. What do you think, LaTanya?

**LaTanya:** They probably wouldn't be all the way up to 80 inches, but there still could be some kids who would be taller.

**Jill:** Yeah, or shorter.

**Teacher:** What if we compare our median height with the median height of the first-grade class? If you look at the shortest height for first grade and fourth grade, the tallest height, and the median height, what can you tell about the two classes? Suppose that that's all you knew about the data—how can these numbers help you compare the first-grade and fourth-grade heights? Talk about this in your pairs for a minute or two.

The teacher records these values:

|  | First grade | Fourth grade |
|---|---|---|
| Shortest | 39 inches | 51 inches |
| Median | 49 inches | 56 inches |
| Tallest | 54 inches | 63 inches |

After the class talks in pairs for a few minutes, the teacher asks for their comments.

**Yuson:** Their median isn't even up to where our inches start.

**Teacher:** So what does that tell you about their class?

**Yuson:** They're a lot shorter.

**Steve:** And even their tallest is shorter.

**Teacher:** What do you mean that even their tallest is shorter?

**Sabrina:** Even their tallest is below our middle person.

**Teacher:** So can anyone say something about the part of our class from the median and up? From 56 to 63 inches? How does that part of our class match the first-grade class?

**Benson:** That whole half of our class is taller than their whole class.

**Abdul:** I have another way to say it. If their class lined up, their whole class would be shorter than our middle, and their line would go down a lot shorter than our line.

In this dialogue, the teacher attempts to move the students away from how to find the median to an explanation of what the median is good for—what it does and does not tell about the data it represents. As the students point out in this discussion, the median does show the middle point of the data, but even if two sets of data have the same median, the data can be spread out in different ways. Using the lowest and highest values along with the median gives a picture of the overall distribution that can help students compare the two data sets.

# Dialogue Box

# Refining a Survey Question

In Session 2.1, students carry out their own survey to compare two groups, using a question of their own choice. Developing and refining their survey questions is an important part of the process of designing their data investigation. As students try out their questions, they find out whether the way they have worded their question results in information that helps them collect useful data. This class is discussing how and why they revised their questions after trying them out with classmates.

**Teacher:** Let's hear the first question you came up with and then your second, because many got revised.

**Lucy:** Our question was "What is your bedtime?" but we found that we had to do "What is your bedtime on a school night?" and then that didn't work and we had to do "How many hours sleep do you get on school nights?"

**Teacher:** What makes you say that your first question and your second didn't work?

**Lucy:** For the first one, people were giving us all different times when we asked it, and they said do you mean on the weekend or what. And the second one people also gave us lots of different times and didn't give us one time. It wasn't numbers—they'd say things like, "Between 8:30 and 10:00." So we decided to ask how many hours of sleep because that would give us just numbers.

**Teacher:** So they were having trouble giving you just one answer, and you tried to change the question so that you would get just one answer. Do you see how their question really changed?

Noemi reports that they didn't have to change their question: How many siblings do you have (including half-siblings and step-siblings)? The teacher surmises that it's because they initially included half and step siblings.

**Teacher:** Can anyone think of any problems or exceptions that might come up with Noemi's question?

**Alejandro:** If they do it in first or second grade, someone might not know what a sibling is.

**Teacher:** They might have to explain that word *sibling*. Can anyone come up with a category that wouldn't be included?

**Ramona:** I live with Ines and she is not really my sister, but I think of her as my sister.

**Teacher:** So would you count her as your sister? [Ramona nods emphatically, "yes."] So does that make any difference for your survey? Does that fit with the information you want?

**Noemi:** No, because we really want to just know if someone is growing up with a lot of other kids or only one or two.

**Teacher:** That makes sense to me. People can decide whether they consider someone a sister or brother. But I have a question for you. If you're interested in whether someone is growing up with a lot of other children, do you want to include any children that live in the house? When I was growing up, my cousin lived with us, so would you want to know that? That's just something for your group to think about. It depends on what you really want to know. Let's hear about another group's question.

**Jake:** We started out with "How many pets at your house?" and that didn't work and then we had "How many four-legged animals do you have at your house?" and then Derek said he had a three-legged frog, so we said "four-legged or supposed to have four legs," but then we ended up with "How many mammals do you have at your house?"

**Teacher:** Why didn't your first question work?

**Jake:** People had fish, and some people had 50 fish, and we didn't really want to count all those. We want to count cats and dogs and things like that.

**Alejandro:** We have two questions. It depends on what class we're doing it in. If it's second grade or under, we'll ask, "How many four-legged animals do you have at home?" But if it's higher we'll ask, "How many mammals do you have at your house?"

A third pair reports their process.

**Emaan:** "How many teeth have you lost since September?" and we were kind of arguing at the beginning, because we were just doing, "How many teeth have you lost?" But we decided we want to know about this year. At first we had "this year" and then we put "since September."

**LaTanya:** Do crowns count? Like if part of your tooth broke off.

Emaan and Bill shake their heads "no."

**LaTanya:** What if you had to have a tooth pulled?

Emaan and Bill shake their heads "no" again.

**Teacher:** So you're talking about a tooth that just naturally falls out and you want to know about differences between first and fourth graders during this school year. That is what you want to find out about. What do you think will happen with the data between the two classes?

**Bill:** I think that fourth graders are growing in more teeth and first graders are losing more.

In this discussion, as students talk about refining their questions, the teacher highlights different reasons for deciding to revise a question. Lucy's group had to make their question clear enough that they would get one answer from each person they asked about bedtime. The teacher helps Noemi's group continue to think about what it is they want to know about number of siblings—is it just the number of brothers and sisters, or is it the number of children in the house? In this case, the teacher also notes that they need to be respectful of people's responses: "People can decide whether they consider someone a sister or brother." Jake and Alejandro do not express completely to the class why they are asking only about mammals, but the teacher knew that they had struggled quite a bit already with their question and decided not to ask them to clarify further. Emaan and Bill changed their question when they realized that they were not interested in the total number of teeth lost by first and fourth graders, but how many are actually lost during first and fourth grades; the teacher asks them for their hypothesis about what they will find out.

# Is This a Good Game?

This fourth-grade class is discussing their responses to the data about Yolanda Griffith and Mwadi Mabika on *Student Activity Book* pages 34 and 35. The teacher starts by asking students what they noticed about Griffith's data to develop some context for considering Problem 2, about whether a game in which Griffith scored 17 points was a good game for her.

**Yuki:** There is one big clump from 15 to 22 that has 20 Xs in it.

**Teacher:** So what does that tell you about Yolanda Griffith's games?

Yuki looks like she does not understand the question.

**Teacher:** I mean, say something about that big clump using words like *games* and *points* instead of *Xs*. Your audience might not know what the *Xs* mean.

**Yuki:** Oh. So those are 20 games.

**Marisol (Yuki's partner):** We were saying that she got 15 to 22 points in a lot of games.

**Teacher:** Did anyone else notice that and have something to say about that clump of data?

**Lucy:** We said the same thing. Also, it's half.

**Teacher:** What do you mean, it's half?

**Lucy:** She played 39 games, so this is 20 games. If she played 40 games, it would be half, so it's more than half.

**Teacher:** So I think what we're learning from Yuki, Marisol, and Lucy's observations is that in about half of Yolanda Griffith's games, really close to half, she scored from 15 to 22 points. So what did you think about Griffith's game on July 5, when she scored 17 points?

**Steve:** It was a good game, because 15 is the median and 17 is higher.

**Cheyenne:** It was good, but it wasn't really good. If she scored 24, it would be really good.

**Derek:** I didn't think it was that good because she's got 13 higher scores.

**Damian:** Yeah, because 27 is her best game.

**Teacher:** What do others think about Derek's argument? He's saying that it wasn't so good because she scored higher in 13 games.

**Cheyenne:** I don't agree. It's still OK. It's above the middle, and there are a lot more games below 17. She knows she can do better, but I think she should be proud of herself because she scored higher than average.

**Enrique:** 15 is in the middle and I think that anything less, well, 4 was her worst day.

**Ursula:** Maybe she was injured that day, or sick, and they didn't put her in for most of the game.

**Tonya:** I think that 13 to 15 is OK, even though it's below the middle, it's still not a bad game, and 15 to 20 is good, and of course beyond that is really good.

**Derek:** It was on the better side, but not her best.

In this discussion, the teacher first asks students to describe Griffith's data in order to help all students refresh themselves about the characteristics of the data and to help some students who had some trouble interpreting the graph. The teacher then focuses on whether a game with 17 points is a good game for Griffith because, according to their written work, the teacher observed that many students in the class have something to say about this question and there are some disagreements between students. As the discussion builds naturally from considering a good game to focus on what is OK, medium, bad, and really good, the discussion gives students the opportunity to look at the shape and spread of the entire data set.

# Dialogue Box

## Discussing Probability Experiments

This fourth-grade class has been working on determining the probability of a variety of events. Then they tried out three probability experiments in which they pulled a cube out of a bag containing two colors of cubes. In Experiment 1, the bag held 10 red cubes and 10 blue cubes. In Experiment 2, the bag held 5 red cubes and 15 blue cubes, and in Experiment 3, there were 15 red cubes and 5 blue cubes in the bag. Students recorded the number of times in 50 trials they pulled a red cube out of the bag (each cube pulled out was placed back in the bag after its color was recorded). In this discussion they are comparing the results with what they predicted would happen.

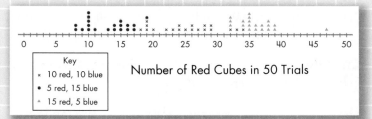

**Teacher:** How do our results for Experiment 1, 10 red cubes and 10 blue cubes in the bag, compare with what we expected?

**Luke:** Most of us got around 23, 24, 25, 26, 27, 28. And that's about what we predicted.

**Cheyenne:** Except for the 34.

**Luke:** No, but remember, we said that it wouldn't work out exactly 25 for everyone, and it didn't. So, we did get what we expected.

**Teacher:** Cheyenne, are you saying that the 34 surprised you? And how about the 18?

**Cheyenne:** The 18 seems like it wouldn't be that hard to get, but the 34 is way, way out there—really far from the rest of the scores, from the 25.

**Marisol:** When we got it, we thought something was wrong with what we did, but we did it again and got 23 the second time.

**Teacher:** Are there any other ways to explain the 34?

**Noemi:** Maybe they counted wrong.

**Richard:** I was keeping track, and I know it was 34.

**Teacher:** Do you think it is impossible to pull out a red cube 34 times out of 50 when you have half red cubes and half blue cubes in the bag?

**Cheyenne:** Not impossible, just not very likely.

**Teacher:** Did anything else surprise you?

**Jake:** Yes. I didn't think anyone would get exactly $\frac{1}{2}$. When Tonya got exactly 25, I was really surprised.

**Teacher:** Why?

**Jake:** Because I thought there was very little chance of getting exactly what you expect. Things hardly ever work out perfectly.

**Damian:** But it's not like the cubes are thinking, "Don't come out exactly even," so 25 should be as likely as any other result.

**Teacher:** Do you think, Damian, that 25 is more likely than other results?

**Damian:** More likely than, say, 30, or 20, but maybe not much different from other scores right around 25.

**Teacher:** Can someone summarize what we found about the half-and-half bag, referring to our line plot?

**Jill:** You don't always get the same thing.

**Teacher:** Can you say that and refer to our results?

**Jill:** We got results all the way from 18 to 34, but most of them were pretty close to 25, in the 20s.

**Abdul:** The results are spread out, but most are in the middle.

**Teacher:** How did the results from the 5 red cubes/ 15 blue cubes experiment compare with the results from the half-and-half experiment?

**Steve:** We got less reds and more blues. The reds are all below 20.

**Teacher:** We talked about this before, but can anyone remind us what we said about 5 reds and 15 blues? It's not half reds. Is there a fraction or a percent you can say that describes the reds, and explain why you chose that fraction? Tonya, I remember you had a way of showing this with the cubes.

**Tonya:** It's one fourth. Here, I can show you with the cubes. If I connect them all together like this, with all the reds first—so I have 20, right? If I break it in half, each half has 10. Now if I break this half in half again, I get all the reds—that's a fourth.

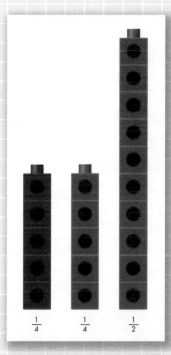

After some further discussion about why the 5 red cubes are $\frac{1}{4}$ or 25 percent of the 20 cubes and why 15 red cubes are $\frac{3}{4}$ or 75 percent of 20 cubes, the teacher goes back to Steve's comment.

**Teacher:** So Steve said that in this experiment, our data shows that people pulled out fewer reds than in the half-and-half experiment. He noticed that the number of reds out of 50 tries was always below 20. Does everyone agree with that statement, or can someone add to what Steve said?

**LaTanya:** I kind of agree. Except they overlap. Like one person got 19 reds in 50 tries when there were only 5 reds in the bag, and that's the same as some people who got 19 when it was half reds in the bag.

**Teacher:** So, there were some overlaps?

**Steve:** Yeah, but generally, there were lower reds in Experiment 2 and more reds in Experiment 3.

**Teacher:** So even though there are some overlaps, do people agree that Steve's statement generally applies?

Most students nod their heads.

**Teacher:** Why do you think it happened that way?

**Noemi:** Because there's just a quarter reds in the bag, that's 25 percent, not 50 percent, so you're not going to pull out a red as often.

**Richard:** There's less chance to pull out red in the $\frac{1}{4}$ bag and more of a chance to pull out a red with the $\frac{3}{4}$ bag. You can see it on the graph. The circles are mostly low, the Xs are in the middle, and the triangles are up higher.

The teacher focused this discussion on comparing the overall shape of the three data sets shown on the graph. The teacher also took the opportunity to review Tonya's good visual model, showing that 5 red cubes are $\frac{1}{4}$ of the total of 20 cubes in the bag. Comparing helps students attend to general features of the results. Students also see that although the results tend to cluster around the expected probability, there is variation. As Jill points out, "You don't always get the same thing. We got results all the way from 18 to 34, but most of them were pretty close to 25, in the 20s."

# Student Math Handbook

The *Student Math Handbook* pages related to this unit are pictured on the following pages. This book is designed to be used flexibly: as a resource for students doing classwork, as a book students can take home for reference while doing homework and playing math games with their families, and as a reference for families to better understand the work their children are doing in class.

When students take the *Student Math Handbook* home, they and their families can discuss these pages together to reinforce or enhance students' understanding of the mathematical concepts and games in this unit.

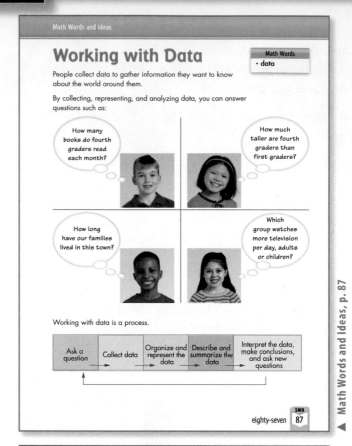

▲ Math Words and Ideas, p. 87

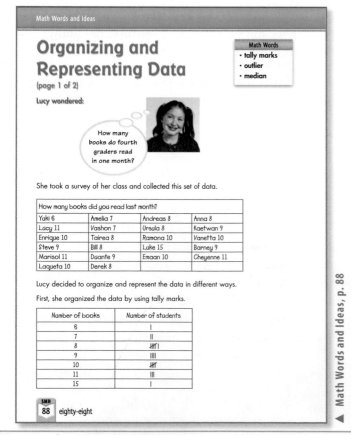

▲ Math Words and Ideas, p. 88

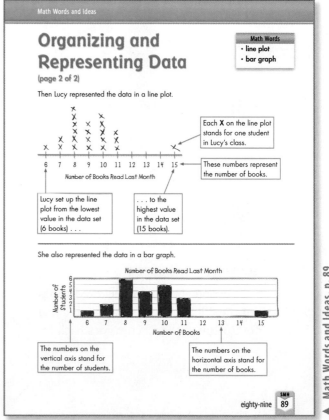

▲ Math Words and Ideas, p. 89

## Math Words and Ideas

# Describing and Summarizing Data (page 1 of 2)

Math Words
- range
- mode

Lucy shared her data with her class.

The teacher asked, "What can you say about the number of books read by students in our class last month?"

Number of Books Read Last Month

Here are some of the students' responses.

Luke noticed the range of this data set.

**Luke:** *The data range from 6 books to 15 books. No one in our class read fewer than 6 books and no one read more than 15 books.*

The **range** is the difference between the highest value and the lowest value in a set of data.

In this data, the range is 9 books.

$$15 - 6 = 0$$

highest value   lowest value   range

Tairea found an interval within which most of the data are concentrated.

**Tairea:** *More than half of the class read between 8 books and 10 books.*

Bill noticed the mode in this data set.

**Bill:** *More people read 8 books than any other number of books.*

The **mode** is the value that occurs most often in a set of data.

**SMH 90** ninety

▲ Math Words and Ideas, p. 90

## Math Words and Ideas

# Describing and Summarizing Data (page 2 of 2)

Math Words
- outlier
- median

Barney noticed an outlier in this data set:

*One person read 15 books and 15 books is far away from the rest of the data. Reading 15 books is unusual for our class, because most people read between 8 and 10 books.*

An **outlier** is a piece of data that has an unusual value, much lower or much higher than most of the data.

Marisol found the median in this data set:

*The median is 9 books. That means that half of the class read 9 books or more.*

The **median** is the middle value of the data when all the data are put in order.

* Look for more information on the Math Words and Ideas page "Finding the Median."

 Consider the outlier in Lucy's data.
What reasons could there be for one student reading 15 books?
What do you think the data show about this class?
If you were writing a newspaper article, what would you report?
What evidence from the data supports your ideas?

ninety one **SMH 91**

▲ Math Words and Ideas, p. 91

## Math Words and Ideas

# Finding the Median (page 1 of 2)

The median is the middle value of the data when all the data are put in order.

Look at these examples.

How many raisins are in a half-ounce box?

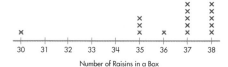

Number of Raisins in a Box

Here are all the data listed in order.

30, 35, 35, 35, 36, 37, 37,   **37,**   37, 37, 38, 38, 38, 38, 38

median

The middle value is **37.**

The median value is **37 raisins.**

*Half of the boxes had 37 raisins or fewer, and half of the boxes had 37 raisins or more.*

**SMH 92** ninety-two

▲ Math Words and Ideas, p. 92

## Math Words and Ideas

# Finding the Median (page 2 of 2)

When a set of data has an even number of values, the median is between the two middle values.

How many books did you read last summer?

Number of Books

Here are all the data listed in order.

12, 13, 13, 14, 14, 14, 15, 15, 15, **16, 17,** 18, 19, 19, 19, 20, 20, 21, 21, 22

median

The middle values are not the same, so the median is midway between the two values 16 and 17. The median is **$16\frac{1}{2}$ books.**

There are as many students in the group who read $16\frac{1}{2}$ books or fewer as there are students who read $16\frac{1}{2}$ books or more.

ninety-three **SMH 93**

▲ Math Words and Ideas, p. 93

## Math Words and Ideas

# Comparing Two Sets
## of Data (page 1 of 4)

Some of Lucy's classmates asked the following question:

How does the number of books read each month by fourth graders compare with the number of books read each month by seventh graders?

They collected data from a seventh grade class.

How many books did you read last month?

| 7 | 3 | 10 | 6 | 6 | 11 | 4 |
| 7 | 6 | 10 | 9 | 11 | 4 | 6 |
| 5 | 5 | 3 | 4 | 6 | 10 | 5 |

They organized the data from the seventh grade class by using tally marks.

| Seventh Grade | |
|---|---|
| Number of books | Number of students |
| 3 | II |
| 4 | IIII |
| 5 | III |
| 6 | IIII |
| 7 | II |
| 10 | III |
| 11 | II |

◄ Math Words and Ideas, p. 94

---

## Math Words and Ideas

**Math Words**
· double bar graph

# Comparing Two Sets
## of Data (page 2 of 4)

Vashon, Duante, Cheyenne, and Yuki created representations to compare the data from the seventh-grade class with the data that Lucy collected from their fourth-grade class.

**Vashon's representation**
Vashon represented each set of data on a line plot:

Number of Books Read Last Month (Fourth Grade)

Number of Books Read Last Month (Seventh Grade)

He used the same scale—from 3 books to 15 books—on both line plots to make it easier to compare them.

**Cheyenne's representation**
Cheyenne represented the data on a double bar graph.

Number of Books Read in a Month

Fourth grade
Seventh grade

Number of Students / Number of Books

◄ Math Words and Ideas, p. 95

---

## Math Words and Ideas

# Comparing Two Sets
## of Data (page 3 of 4)

**Duante's representation**
Duante made a line plot and used the numbers 4 and 7 instead of **X**s to represent the students in the different grades.

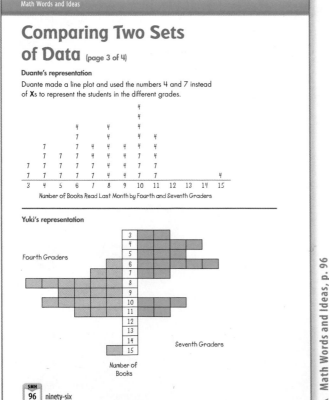

Number of Books Read Last Month by Fourth and Seventh Graders

**Yuki's representation**

Fourth Graders

Seventh Graders

Number of Books

◄ Math Words and Ideas, p. 96

---

## Math Words and Ideas

# Comparing Two Sets
## of Data (page 4 of 4)

The students looked at their representations of the data they collected and compared the numbers of books read in one month by fourth graders and by seventh graders.

Here is what they noticed.

**Vashon:** *The lowest number of books a fourth grader read is 6 books. More than half of the seventh-grade students read 6 books or fewer.*

**Duante:** *The median in the seventh-grade data (6 books) is lower than the median in the fourth-grade data (9 books).*

**Cheyenne:** *The fourth-grade data are clustered mostly between 8 books and 10 books. Most of the seventh-grade data are clustered between 3 books and 7 books.*

**Yuki:** *One fourth grader read more books than any of the seventh graders.*

Based on what they noticed in the data they compared, Vashon, Duante, Cheyenne, and Yuki came to these conclusions:

Our data show that, overall, the fourth-grade students read more books than the seventh-grade students. The median value for seventh graders was lower than the median value for fourth graders. Even though one fourth grader read more books than anyone, that wasn't typical of all the fourth graders. More than half the seventh graders read 6 or fewer books, which is the lowest number read by a fourth grader.

Maybe the books that seventh graders read are longer than the books that fourth graders read. Maybe seventh graders have more homework than we do, and they don't have time to read. Maybe they don't have good books in their room like we do.

 What new survey question could these students ask next to get more information about the reading habits of fourth and seventh graders?

◄ Math Words and Ideas, p. 97

---

# Probability (page 1 of 3)

**How likely is it . . . ?  What are the chances . . . ?**

Probability is the study of measuring how likely it is that something will happen. Sometimes we estimate probability on the basis of data and experience about how the world works.

Some future events are impossible, based on what we know about the world.

The entire Pacific Ocean will freeze this winter.

Some future events are certain.

The sun will rise tomorrow.

The probability of many other events falls between impossible and certain.

No one in our class will be absent tomorrow.

It will rain next weekend.

**Likelihood Line**

Impossible          Maybe          Certain

A                                    B

 Can you think of events that can go at points A and B on the likelihood line?

---

# Probability (page 2 of 3)

In some situations, there is a certain number of equally likely outcomes. In these situations, you can find the probability of an event by looking at how many different ways it can turn out.

What will happen if you toss a coin?

There are two possible outcomes. You can get heads or tails. If the coin is fair, there is a 1 out of 2 chance that you will get heads and a 1 out of 2 chance that you will get tails.

What can happen if you roll a number cube marked with the numbers 1, 2, 3, 4, 5, and 6?

There are six possible outcomes. If the number cube is fair, every number is just as likely to come up as any other number.

The probability of getting a five is 1 out of 6.

What is the chance of rolling an even number?

| 1 | 2 |
|---|---|
| 3 | 4 |
| 5 | 6 |

There are 3 even numbers out of 6 possibilities. So, there is a 3 out of 6 chance of rolling an even number.

You can also say that this is a 1 out of 2 chance.

What can happen if you pull a marble out of a jar that contains 3 yellow marbles and 9 blue marbles?

There are 12 marbles in the jar. The chance of pulling out a blue marble is 9 out of 12.

You can also say this is a 3 out of 4 chance.

---

# Probability (page 3 of 3)

In mathematics, you can use numbers from 0 to 1 to describe the probability of an event.

The probability of an impossible event is 0.

The probability of a certain event is 1.

The probability of an event that is equally likely to happen or not happen is $\frac{1}{2}$.

For example, when you flip a fair coin there is a 1 out of 2 chance that you will get heads. The probability of getting heads is $\frac{1}{2}$.

Probabilities can fall anywhere from 0 to 1.

0                    $\frac{1}{2}$                    1

C          D

The chance of spinning an even number on this spinner is 0.

The chance of rolling a number cube and getting a five is 1 out of 6 or $\frac{1}{6}$.

The chance of pulling a blue marble out of this jar is $\frac{9}{12}$ or $\frac{3}{4}$.

The chance of spinning an odd number on this spinner is 1.

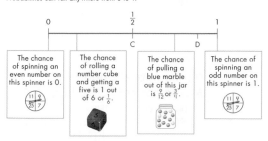

 Describe events that can go at points C and D on the line. You can use the idea of a spinner, a number cube, or pulling marbles out of a jar.

# Index

## A

**Analysis of data,** 10–11, 72–73
**Argument development,** 44–45, 82–83, 88, 89–90, 118
**Assessment**
  activities, 50, 63–64, 118, 127–129, 136–138, 139–143
  benchmarks, 15, 63, 118, 127–129, 136–138, 139–143
  checklists, 63
  End-of-Unit Assessment, 15, 117–119, 136–138
  ongoing. *See* Ongoing Assessment: Observing Students at Work.
  portfolio opportunities, 14
  Teacher Notes, 127–129, 136–138, 139–143
  writing opportunities, 14
**Assessment in This Unit,** 14–15

## B

**Bar graphs.** *See* Graphs.
**Benchmarks,** 15, 63–64, 118, 127–129, 136–138, 139–143

## C

**Categorical data,** 57, 130
**Certainty,** 12, 96–100, 103, 134–135
**Checklists,** 15, 63
**Collecting data,** 25, 31–33, 37–38, 63–65, 109–111, 114, 118, 131
**Comparing**
  data, 10–11, 118
  groups of data, 42–45, 83–86, 123–124, 141–143
  medians of height data, 49
  number of cavities, 50, 127–129
  probability experiment data, 115–116

## D

**Data.** *See also* Surveys.
  analyzing, 10–11, 72–73
  collecting, 25, 31–33, 37–38, 63–65, 109–111, 114, 118, 131
  comparing, 10–11, 31, 42–45, 49–50, 83–86, 115–116, 118, 123–124, 141–143

describing, 10–11, 26, 28–29, 43–45, 76–80, 82–83, 118, 121–122, 127–129, 139–141, 144–145
  designing an investigation, 11
  developing arguments from, 82–83, 88, 89–90, 118
  finding the median, 47–48
  implementing an investigation, 11
  interpreting, 11, 76, 83–86, 88, 139–141, 146–148, 151
  landmarks, 83
  link to probability, 95
  numerical and categorical, 57, 130
  organizing, 10, 26–27
  predictions made from, 25, 35, 95, 104–105
  recording, 110–111, 118
  reporting, 27, 73–74, 78
  representing, 10, 25–28, 33, 38–40, 65–66, 68–70, 77–80, 83–86, 114, 118, 121
  shape of, 29, 44, 123–124, 144–145
**Describing data,** 10–11, 26, 28–29, 33–34, 43–45, 76–80, 82–83, 118, 121–122, 127–129, 139–141, 144–145
**Dialogue Boxes,** 144–153
  Describing the Shape of the Raisin Data, 144–145
  Discussing Probability Experiments, 152–153
  Is This a Good Game?, 151
  Refining a Survey Question, 149–150
  What Does the Median Tell You?, 147–148
  What Is a Typical Height?, 146
**Differentiation: Supporting the Range of Learners,** 18
  English Language Learners (ELL), 18, 23, 58, 99
  Extension, 18, 40, 80, 111
  Intervention, 18, 40, 64, 79, 86, 88–89, 106, 111

## E

**End-of-Unit Assessment,** 15, 117–119, 136–138, 139–143
**English Language Learners (ELL),** 18, 23, 58, 99
**English units,** 31
**Extension,** 18, 40, 80, 111

## F

**Family Letters,** 29, 35
**Fractions**
  describing data with, 34
  representing likelihood, 103–106, 108–109, 118, 134–135
**Frequency distribution,** 121

## G

**Graphs**
  bar, 26, 68
  line plots, 121
    interpretation of, 144–148
    of Mystery Data, 82–83
    of probability experiments, 114
    representing data on, 26–27, 33, 77–78, 84–85

## I

**Impossibility,** 12, 95–100, 103, 134–135
**Interpreting data,** 11, 76, 83–86, 88, 139–141, 146–148, 151
**Intervention,** 18, 40, 64, 79, 86, 88–89, 106, 111
**Investigations Curriculum,** 6–7

## L

**Landmarks in data,** 83
**Likelihood Line,** 136–138
  events on, 95–100, 105–106
  numbers representing probability, 102–106, 108–109
**Line plots.** *See* Graphs.
**LogoPaths software,** 13

## M

**Mathematical Emphases,** 15, 19, 51, 91
**Mathematics in This Unit,** 10–12
**Math Focus Points,** 10–12, 16, 19, 22, 30, 36, 41, 46, 51, 56, 62, 67, 71, 75, 81, 87, 91, 94, 101, 107, 113, 117
  for Discussion, 28, 33, 43, 48, 60, 68, 74, 76, 82, 89, 99, 102, 108, 115
**Math Notes**
  Describing the Data, 43, 82
  Fractions, 34

In-between Events, 100
Landmarks in Data, 83
Looking at the Values, 28
Measurement Tools, 31
The Middle of the Data, 48
Personal Experience, 98
Probability, 95
Two Aspects to Probability, 104
Understanding Probability, 110
**Measurement**
of first graders' height, 37–38
of heights of classmates, 31–33
of long lengths, 13
**Median**
finding and using, 47–50, 77, 121,
125–126
information from, 138–141, 147–148
of Mystery Data B and C, 82–83
**Mode,** 121, 122

**N**

**Numerical data,** 57, 130

**O**

**Observing Students at Work.** *See*
Ongoing Assessment: Observing
Students at Work.
**One**
representing certainty, 103–106,
108–109, 118, 134–135
**Ongoing Assessment: Observing
Students at Work,** 14, 27–28, 33, 38,
40, 42–43, 48, 60, 64, 65, 66, 70, 73,
78, 85, 88, 99, 105–106, 111, 115
**Outcomes,** 95
**Outliers,** 83, 121, 122
**Overview of This Unit,** 8–9

**P**

**Planners**
Investigation Planners, 20–21, 52–55,
92–93
Today's Plan, 22, 30, 36, 41, 46, 56,
62, 67, 71, 75, 81, 87, 94, 101, 107,
113, 117
**Polls,** 95
**Portfolio opportunities,** 14

**Practice and Review in This Unit,** 17
**Predictions,** 25, 35, 95, 104–105
**Probability**
description of, 12
experimental vs. theoretical, 12,
104–105, 109–111, 134–135
experiments with, 109–111, 114–116,
152–153
Likelihood Line, 95–99, 102–106,
108–109, 136–138
with multiple possible outcomes,
108–109
numerical representation, 102–105
**Professional Development.** *See*
Dialogue Boxes; Teacher Notes.
**Program Components,** 6–7

**Q**

**Quick Survey.** *See* Ten-Minute Math.

**R**

**Range,** 43, 82–83, 121
**Recording**
data, 118
probability trials, 109–111
**Reporting data,** 27, 73–74, 78
**Representation**
of class height data, 33
of data, 10, 121–122
of first-grader height data, 38–40
of groups of data, 38–40, 65–66,
68–70
interpretation of, 76–77
likelihood of events, 118
line plots, 121
of Mystery Data B and C, 77–80
of probability experiments, 114
of raisins in a box data, 25–28
of weather data, 118
of WNBA players' data, 83–86

**S**

**Student Math Handbook minis,**
154–157
**Supporting the Range of Learners.**
*See* Differentiation: Supporting the
Range of Learners.

**Surveys**
data collection with, 63–65
questions for, 57–60, 149–150
*Quick Survey. See* Ten-Minute Math.

**T**

**Teacher Notes,** 121–143
About the Mystery Data, 132–133
Assessment: Comparing Numbers
of Cavities, 127–129
Collecting Data from Other
Classes, 131
Data Terms and Representations,
121–122
End-of-Unit Assessment Problem 1:
Likelihood Events, 136–140
End-of-Unit Assessment Problem 2:
Was It Hotter in Philadelphia or
Boston?, 141–143
Finding and Using the Median,
125–126
Focusing on the Shape of the Data,
123–124
Impossible, Certain, and Everything
in Between, 134–135
Numerical and Categorical Data, 130
**Teaching Notes**
Audience, 69
Certainty, 97
Choose One Question, 88
Describing Data, 28
Finding the Median, 47
First-Grade Data, 37
Making an Argument, 88
Marking Heights, 31
Measurement Tools, 32
Reported Data, 78
Revealing the Mysteries, 83
Revising Survey Questions, 60
Save the Height Data, 33
Time Adjustment, 63
Understanding Representations, 76
Vocabulary, 34
Working in Pairs, 59, 84
Writing Project, 72
**Technology Notes**
Getting Started with *LogoPaths*
Software, 13

**Ten-Minute Math,** 13, 16
    *Quick Survey,* 16, 21, 41, 46, 53, 67, 87,
        93, 107, 113
    *Today's Number: Broken Calculator,*
        16, 21, 23, 30, 36, 53, 56, 62, 71, 75,
        81, 93, 94, 101, 117
**Ten-Minute Math in This Unit,** 16
**Today's Number.** *See* Ten-Minute
    Math.

## V

**Value,** 76, 82–83, 121
**Vocabulary,** 121–122
    bar graph, 26, 68
    conclusion, 72

    data, 25, 38
    line plot, 26, 68
    median, 47
    numerical data, 57
    outlier, 34
    probability, 95, 102
    representation, 38
    survey, 57
    value, 83

## W

**Writing opportunities,** 14

## Z

**Zero**
    representing impossibility, 103–106,
        108–109, 118, 134–135